Cover:
In the style of El Greco
ST. PETER
Oil on canvas, 28.7 x 22.6 in.
Doerner-Institut, Munich

FAKES AND FORGERIES

The Minneapolis Institute of Arts

July 11–September 29, 1973

ACKNOWLEDGMENTS

In the course of researching an exhibition over a four year period a great many debts are incurred to those persons who have been generous with their time and advice. It is always difficult to properly express one's thanks, but especially so in the case of this exhibition; much of the information by definition is confidential in nature. It is, thus, that perhaps the most profound gratitude is aimed at those who appear here merely as "anonymous."

Exhibitions require immense amounts of support and the staff of The Minneapolis Institute of Arts has given in extraordinary measure of their talents and energies. These are particularly difficult times for this museum, being away from its normal home, but everyone has pulled together to produce a show that by rights could not have been done given the time and manpower available. Special thanks are due, however, to the following: Evan Maurer, Curator, without whose diligence and devotion the exhibition surely would not have occurred; Jo Ann Reedquist, Exhibitions Coordinator, for the same reasons; Russell Colber, Communications Director, Roger Feuerman and Nancy Rice of Knox-Reeves, for insuring our audience; Ellen Bradbury, Registrar, for logistical excellence; Irwin Lucius, Vern Blanck and Robert Pratt for ingenious installation.

Also deeply involved were: Ruth Dean, Designer; Susan Brown, Editor; Judy Sobol and Stephanie Beck, Tours and Docents; Gary Sherman and Carroll T. Hartwell, Photographers; Judy Shen-Dar, Kathryn C. Johnson, Darlene Plathe, Mary Marfield, Researchers; Margaret Olson, Mary Nazarenko, Robert Cohen, and Marilyn Bjorkland, Secretaries.

Entries in the catalog in various specialties have been supplied in part or in toto by: Evan Maurer, African, Oceanic, Oriental; David McFadden, Decorative Arts; Arnold Jolles, Conservation; Ellen Bradbury, Pre-Columbian.

All those listed below have in one measure or another made this exhibition a possibility: Anonymous Lenders; Helene Adhemar; American Museum of Natural History, New York; Amon Carter Museum, Fort Worth; Associated American Artists, New York; Janet M. Backhouse; Bayerischen Staatsgemäldesammlungen, Munich; The John Nelson Bergstrom Art Center and Museum, Neenah, Wisconsin; Museum of Fine Arts, Boston; Germain Bazin; Bernard V. Bothmer; Prof. Dr. Peter Bloch; Mr. and Mrs. Atherton Bean; Alan Brandt, Inc., New York; The Brooklyn Museum; Charles M. Brooks; Charles E. Buckley; Marian Burleigh-Motley; James Byam-Shaw; Mr. and Mrs. Benton J. Case, Jr.; Mrs. Jack W. Casper; R.J. Charleston; The Art Institute of Chicago; The Cleveland Museum of Art; John D. Cooney; The Corning Museum of Glass, Corning, N.Y.; Courtauld Institute of Art, London; Mr. and Mrs. John Cowles, Sr.; H. van Crimpen; A. Croft-Murray; The Detroit Institute of Arts; Doerner-Institut, Munich; Keith Domes; Prof. Noel Duval; Edward H. Dwight; Gordon Eckholm; Viktor Elbern; Joseph Faulkner; Sarah Faunce; Richard Fazzini; David B. Findlay Gallery, New York; Peter Findlay; Mr. and Mrs. Miles Q. Fiterman; Fogg Art Museum, Cambridge, Massachusetts; The Free Library of Philadelphia;

Signora Bona Frescobaldi; Martin Friedman; Henry G. Gardiner; John Gere; Robert H. Glauber; Noah Goldowsky; Noah Goldowsky, Inc., New York; Carmen Gómez-Moreno; Martin Gordon; Luigi Grassi; Edward H. Hamm; Peter Hassrick; Howell J. Heaney; Jack Hillier; Hirschl and Adler Galleries, New York; The Museum of Fine Arts, Houston; Charles F. Hummel; Institute of Fine Arts, New York University; Donald Jenkins; Harold Joachim; John G. Johnson Collection, Philadelphia; Frances F. Jones; Mrs. Paul E. Jones; Stephen Rees Jones; Robert Kashey; Kasser Art Foundation, Montclair, New Jersey; John W. Keefe; Ronald Klapmeier; A. J. B. Kiddell; J. J. Klejman; Otto Kurz; Michel Laclotte; Michael Levey; Loewi-Robertson, Inc., Los Angeles; Musée du Louvre, Paris; Galerie du Jeu de Paume, Paris; Ann T. Lurie; Dorothy L. Lytle; Lawrence Majewski; James H. Maroney; John Maxon; Austin L. McLean; Mr. and Mrs. Charles B. Meech; Menil Foundation, Houston; The Metropolitan Museum of Art; Prof. Ulrich Middledorf; Minnesota Historical Society, St. Paul; Agnes Mongan; Philippe de Montebello; Munson-Williams-Proctor Institute, Utica, New York; Douglas Newton; Dr. Thomas D. Nicholson; S. Nystad; Konrad Oberhüber; Mr. and Mrs. Patrick O'Rourke; Philadelphia Museum of Art; The Phillips Collection, Washington, D.C.; E.P. Pillsbury; Mr. and Mrs. Carroll C. Pratt; The Museum of Primitive Art, New York; The Art Museum, Princeton University; O. P. Reed, Jr.; Mr. and Mrs. Robert Riesberg; Rijksmuseum, Amsterdam; Rijksmuseum Vincent van Gogh, Amsterdam; Joseph Rishel; Daniel Robbins; Mr. and Mrs. William J. Robertson; Pierre Rosenberg; Herwarth Rottgen; Merrill Rueppel; Helmut Ruhemann; Mr. and Mrs. David Ryan; The St. Louis Art Museum; Fred R. Salisbury; Dr. W. Sandberg; Fine Arts Gallery of San Diego; Alan R. Sawyer; M.R. Schweitzer; Schweitzer Gallery, New York; Shepherd Gallery, Associates, New York; Staatliche Museen Preussischer Kulturbesitz, Berlin; Dr. Hanns Swarzenski; William S. Talbot; Dr. P. J. J. van Thiel; Janet Thomas; Margery E. Torrey; P.O. Troutman, D.H.H. Turner; University of Minnesota Libraries, Minneapolis; Dr. A. F. E. Van Schendel; Cornelius Vermeule; Robert C. Vose, Jr.; Walker Art Center, Minneapolis; Alan Wardwell; Ellis Waterhouse; Ben Weinreb; Mr. and Mrs. Leon Wilburne; Kenneth M. Wilson; Henry Francis DuPont Winterthur Museum, Winterthur, Delaware; Otto Wittman; Dr. Christian Wolters; Willis Woods; Rudy Wunderlich; Yale University Art Gallery, New Haven, Connecticut; William Young.

S.S.II

INTRODUCTION

This exhibition has been four years in the making and could probably have gone on for four more. The subject is fascinating, and some of the most interesting facets have never been published. Stories, discoveries, and recollections are often, by nature, confidential, but as time progresses old wounds inflicted on hapless egos by eager fakers heal and new material emerges. A decade or so from now someone will show us the mistakes we made.

Friedländer said we laugh at the errors of our parents and our children will laugh at us. But this is not a laughing matter. Much of the material shown here was created to deceive and deceive it did, but we can profit from the lessons to be learned. How better to see what the qualities of a great original work of art are than to see what they are not.

In the selection of this exhibition objects were chosen to represent a specific type or style of fraud. To be sure there were disappointments as many desired objects could not or would not be lent. Fakes of works by French artists, for example, cannot be lent from France for the law requires that they be destroyed. For the most part, however, we are satisfied.

The visitor will note that there are scarcely any "modern" fakes. The reasons are two: first the subject is still too touchy and few will yet admit to error; but perhaps more important, fakes of our own time are the hardest to "see" for we ourselves are too close to them, too much a part of them to feel the qualitative difference. When Andy Warhol often does not paint his own pictures, who is to say what a fake is.

Thus you are invited to look and learn. Know what you see, feel what you see, but most of all see. Too often we only look. Here, we hope, is the chance to connect the eye and the mind in a way not normally available in museum exhibitions or, for that matter, museums.

Samuel Sachs, II

FAKES, FORGERIES, AND OTHER DECEPTIONS

THE CLIMATE FOR FRAUD

The purpose of this exhibition is primarily educational; that is, to familiarize the public with various forms of forgery and fraud in the fine arts and to demonstrate the basic methods of detection used by museums and collectors. In addition, however, the exhibition is intended to engage the viewer in a personal dialogue with works of art, both real and fake, and to explore the subtleties and nuances of perception, intuition, and scholarly knowledge that make any encounter with art a dynamic experience.

The social conditions and realities of human character which underlie the phenomenon of art forgery are worth noting. The principle motivating factor is, of course, profit, but, significantly, this is as true of the prospective buyer as it is of the forger. Thomas P. F. Hoving, Director of The Metropolitan Museum of Art, has said, "Whether you're a private person or a museum, your mood can be categorized in three words: speed, need, greed...The confidence game, which is part of the forger's game, is based on crawling greed."[1] Forty-four modern masters, faked by the now-famous Hungarian Elmyr de Hory, were purchased for endowment to Southern Methodist University by Algur Hurtle Meadows who boasted that he had got them for a few thousand dollars less than the asking prices[2]

It is generally agreed that art forgery operates, like any other industry, on a supply and demand basis. When the demand outstrips the supply, certain items become rare and desirable and therefore of interest to the forger. There are other reasons, less common, for art forgery. For example, in the 18th century the Scot, James Macpherson, faked the epic Gaelic poems of Ossian in an attempt to bestow upon his country the dignity of an ancient, civilized past[3] Some forgeries belong to the realm of practical joke or test of the connoisseur's knowledge and eye. Such was the case with the legendary cupid carved at the suggestion of Lorenzo de' Medici by the young Michelangelo (1475-1546) and sold by a Roman dealer to the well-known collector of antiquities, Cardinal Riario, as a genuine antique[4] The cardinal was fooled, and Michelangelo had the distinction of being proved as good a sculptor as the ancients.

VARIOUS FORMS OF FRAUD

The true art fraud (the law does not distinguish between "fake," "forgery," and "deception") involves the intention to deceive, the attempt to pass a product of artistic character off as the work of a different hand or of a different period. Most often this intention to deceive originates not with the artist but rather with the dealer/middleman; thus, there are many, perhaps a majority, of instances of "forgeries without forgers." The essence of art forgery, then, is not necessarily imitation. Authorities have distinguished the following categories of art fraud; combinations of categories are also possible:

I. An exact copy of a specific original.

A true forgery is a copy done by someone other than the original artist with the intent to pass it off as the original. This has been a practice since ancient Roman times when the demand for things Greek had political as well as cultural significance. The German Renaissance master, Albrecht Durer (1471-1528), was forced to seek redress from the courts of both Venice and Nuremberg where his "handiwork" was being "fraudulently reproduced."[5] In the former city copyists were forbidden to use Durer's monogram, and in the latter the marketing of imitation Durers was prohibited. The French landscape painter, Claude Lorrain (1600-1682), attempted to prevent such counterfeiting by publishing his **Liber Veritas (Book of Truth)** containing sketches of all his works together with notes on the whereabouts of each item[6] Unfortunately Claude did not include everything, and there are still debates about which of two drawings is really from his hand.

A workshop copy can be from the hand of the master himself (Leonardo da Vinci produced a duplicate of the **Madonna of the Rocks**), by workshop assistants apprenticed to and painting in the style of the master, or by a collaboration of assistants and the master. Such was the case with the vast majority of works produced by the Flemish painter/diplomat, Peter Paul Rubens (1577-1640). In former times a painter's studio was considered more akin to a workshop than a sacred precinct of genius, and Rubens made no attempt to deceive the buyer. For example, in 1618 he wrote to Sir Dudley Carlton in regard to a duplicate painting, "As this reproduction is not yet quite completed, I am going to retouch it throughout myself. So it can pass for an original if necessary." Regarding other copies, he continued, "I have retouched them to such effect that they can hardly be distinguished from the originals...they are perfect miracles at the price."[7] Rarely, these studio copies are distinguished as such, as in the case of the four or five replicas of most of El Greco's paintings noted in the studio inventory made after his death. Some were expressly distinguished by the words, "This is the original."[8] It is in this category that positive attributions are especially difficult.

Both the student copy made in the course of traditional academic art training and the copy made by a professional copyist (generally commissioned by someone who could not afford the original and clearly labelled or designated as a copy) run the risk of falling into dishonest hands and later being passed off as originals. There is especial confusion in the area of prints and reproductions.

Before the invention of photography a popular means of distributing famous painted images was by multiple editions of engravings, etchings, or later lithographs, distillations of paintings into the black and white medium of prints. The honest craftsmen who engraved or etched the plates called themselves "translators" and clearly identified themselves as such on the plates and, therefore, on every image. Modern forgers can, of course, tamper with the "translator's" mark.

A final variation on the copy, involving compromising signatures, arises as a result of the generosity of artists. The ancient Greeks, Apelles the painter (4th century B.C.) and Phidias the sculptor (5th century B.C.) signed their names to the work of favored students in order to help them in their careers[9]. The French Rococo painter, Francois Boucher (1703-1770), is recorded to have signed the especially successful copies made by students of his own drawings[10]. In the same manner Jean-Baptiste-Camille Corot (1796-1875), the French landscape painter whose reputation is plagued perhaps more than any other painter in history by the existence of countless forgeries, signed the work of students, followers, admirers, and especially, destitute young artists upon whom he took pity.

II. The deliberate fabrication or fake.

The pastiche is a composition based on fragments or portions of existing works of art. For example, the forger can combine the hands from one portrait by Hans Holbein the Younger, the head from another, and the fur shawl from still another. The resultant painting, a pastiche or "mixture," certainly presents itself to the prospective buyer with some knowledge as a "Holbein."

The evocation, or work of art "in the manner of" some famous artist, is a more subtle and ingenious form of a deliberate fabrication and most of the well-known forgers of the 19th and 20th centuries engaged in this type of forgery. The forger attempts to create an object in the style and manner of another time. Clifford Irving, now himself an infamous forger, observed of the Hungarian art forger, Elmyr de Hory, that "he chose his subjects exclusively from the period he understood best — he was a product of the same epoch, the same European background, the same schools of artistic thinking…and he only painted subjects for which he had, as he put it, 'an affinity.'"[11] The "evocation" seems especially detectable with the passage of a reasonable span of time because, as every authority points out, every culture, every distinct period in history has its own feeling, its own "field of force."

All forgeries "in the manner of" another time, then, cannot escape containing something of their own time. It is this combination of the old style and harmony with the contemporary that makes forgeries of this type so attractive at first. Mark Twain, after having visited the great European galleries and museums, remarked that the modern copies of old masterpieces were always more pleasant to look at than the originals![12] Forgeries, then, even forgeries of ancient works, tend to cater to contemporary tastes.

III. The deliberate misattribution.

At its most unimaginative this type of art fraud consists of simply claiming that something is something else. For example, a perfectly uninspired, 19th-century painting of two figures in dark clothing could be identified by an unscrupulous dealer as a work by Edouard Manet (1832-1883). The knowledgeable buyer would know in an instant that the painting looked nothing at all like a Manet. Questions of judgment are complicated when the unscrupulous dealer or forger adds a signature or other identifying mark associated with a famous artist. The addition of an important signature is the single most prevalent form of art fraud and the one that takes the least talent or effort. Certain passages can be added or, if they are a giveaway to the actual date and identity of the work, painted out. Inscriptions alluding to a famous person or collection can be added, giving the painting a further aura of importance and authenticity.

IV. The honest mistattribution.

Here the question of "faking" is not involved. This is the realm of "followers" or members of a master's workshop who imitated the master closely in subject matter and style and who are called, collectively, a "school." Their work is sometimes striking enough to be considered that of the master himself. This is, by and large, honest work and is considered less valuable than that of a famous master only because of the buying public's infatuation with certain names.

THE FORGERS' METHODS

The forging of modern, late 19th and 20th century, paintings is relatively simple if the forger is moderately competent and can create a convincing evocation of a famous painter's style. Forging an old master, however, involves a great deal more thought and care and actual research into the methods and materials of the past. First the forger must find a worthless old canvas whose discoloration from age is immediately visible on the back. In addition, the threads of the canvas will be pulled into a wavy pattern corresponding to the nails holding it to the stretcher. The old canvas also comes with old priming, a surface broken up by cracks and fissures of age called "craquelure," and, possibly, even a genuine old frame. All of these things will help in creating the illusion of age and again illustrate that the essence of art forgery is the intent to deceive.

The forger of a modern painting need not worry about an especially aged-looking canvas, nor does he have to be careful about the kinds of paints and mediums he uses, for modern materials are mass-produced, by and large chemically produced, and uniform in quality. The forger of an old painting, however, must know which kinds of pigments were used in which periods of history, which binders, mediums, kinds of varnish, etc., if he wishes to escape detection. Han van Meegeren, the famous forger of the early works of Vermeer of Delft (1632-1675), used old badger-hair brushes to apply genuine white lead, rather than zinc white which replaced white lead in the 18th century, and organic lapis lazuli rather than modern cobalt blue as his blue pigment![3] The determined forger must know how to manufacture these pigments himself, as they are not available in art supply shops.

The medium, that is the substance in which the pigments are suspended and in which form they are spread onto the canvas, is as crucial to the forger's success because the medium affects the length of drying time and the way in which the surface will imitate age. Genuine "craquelure" is the result of the uneven movements of the support (canvas) caused by the natural shrinkage of the medium on aging. Genuine oil paintings take many, many years to dry to a state so hard that they cannot be dissolved with alcohol. In their attempts to speed up this hardening process forgers have resorted to all kinds of combinations of glue, varnish, heat, and, in the case of van Meegeren again, a modern resinous substance similar to bakelite![4] A real, though not old, craquelure can be obtained by heating and rolling the canvas, as the new paint will break along the same lines as the old underpainting. Less ingenious forgers incise the cracks and lines with a needle, and some even draw them on the surface with a lead pencil or black ink. Naturally, the expert begins his examination of a suspect painting with a careful examination of the surface.

The forgery of drawings is relatively less complicated, old paper being the essential ingredient in terms of materials. This is usually obtained from old ledgers with blank pages purchased from second-hand book-shops. In the realm of drawings, especially, forgers make copies, that is, virtual duplicates of genuine works of art in a medium which is different from the original. For example, an original watercolour is rendered by the forger in coloured chalk. There are also many examples of watercolour and pastel forgeries of modern oil paintings. Something "gets lost" in the translation, and the prospective buyer may not be quite so suspicious that he has seen that particular work of art before.

The various print media, especially engravings, etchings, and litho-graphs, have since the times of their respective inventions posed peculiar problems due to their very nature, that is, as mechanical means to produce a number of identical images. Before photography either the forger had to re-work a worn-out original plate or re-engrave or re-etch the copied image, and therefore, there were discernible differences between the original and the forgery. Since the invention of photography, however, the exact image can be reproduced by photo-mechanical means, and forged signatures can be easily added to these prints. The major distinction between a genuine print, etching, engraving, or litho-graph, whether it is old or new, and the forgery is to be detected in the surface quality of the lines and inked passages.

Cast metal sculpture presents the same opportunity for unauthorized reproduction as do the print media. Editions of figures cast in bronze often number as many as six, all considered genuine, although the French sculptor, Auguste Rodin (1840-1917), considered only the original and one cast of any of his pieces to be genuine."[15] Modern forgers of bronze sculpture must create the same look of age as must the forger of an old painting. The sometimes encrusted, but generally dark and mellow, surface appearance of an old bronze is called "patina." There are standard formulas for creating an aged appearance to new metal over a matter of days or weeks with modern chemicals. Forgers intending to carve works "in the manner of" some old master often utilize old marble, perhaps even whole statues, which they recarve, thereby destroying the old figure. The same is true of carvers of wood. Again chemicals, primarily acids, can give to newly carved marble the look of hundreds of years, and wood can be selectively mutilated and rubbed to look worn.

All other kinds of art objects from Renaissance jewels to Egyptian mummies can be and have been faked. Chinese bronze vessels, medieval enamels and ivories, silver, glass and chinaware, but especially antique furniture are all attractive subjects to the forger. Especially to be watched for are items that were originally more-or-less mass-produced, such as pressed glass and simple, functional furniture designs. They are as easily faked as they were once produced, and all the marks of mass-production, such as mold seams on glassware or modern lathe marks on chair legs, correspond to the original. On the other hand, equally profitable to the forger is the fraudulent copy of a very rare, very expensive single piece whose phenomenal market value would render still profitable the thousands of dollars and hours spent on the painstaking, by-hand forgery of the item.

METHODS OF DETECTION

There are two distinct approaches to the detection of art forgeries and fakes. The first, often referred to as intuition or expertise, is the accumulated experience and sensitivity that creates the phenomenon of connoisseurship. The term implies not only knowledge of facts but also wisdom and objectivity. This is generally the first phase in the examination of works of art by prospective buyers, be they important reputable dealers, representatives of museums, or knowledgeable collectors. It is chiefly a matter of the trained eye looking at the surface and style of the object and relating that visual information to all past knowledge of such objects, either mentally or in actual comparisons of the suspect object with originals of the same type or by the same artist. Especially in the case of the facsimile copy, experts agree that the fake, having about it something that is of its own time and, therefore, perhaps missing the elusive quality of the original, will be readily unmasked. In addition to the forgery's lack of stylistic unity, it is generally agreed that copies, being produced in a backwards sort of process from finished object to all the underlying preparations, exhibit an anxiety and a lack of ease that are readily apparent. Further, a true work of art is created out of emotion and in harmony with its place in time and space. The forger, in the words of Hans Tietze, "…reproduces somebody else's emotion…If he follows his model slavishly the constraint will be very strong; if he allows himself some freedom he runs the risk of making mistakes…"[16] This lack of spontaneity and rhythmic integration of all parts is the major indicator to the trained eye that the object is not genuine.

There are a growing number of scientific laboratory processes and tests which can be applied to a suspected forgery. Among these are photographic prints made with ultraviolet and infrared light rays which reveal the substructure of the painting and various kinds of light ray analyses (x-ray diffraction, x-ray spectroscopy, infrared spectroscopy, and liquid and gas chromatography) which present quantitative data in the form of graphs or photographs. These latter processes require expensive equipment and highly trained personnel. Less complex chemical analyses of materials used in paintings and sculpture, in addition to the simple application of alcohol to the surface of a painting, are more typical of the resources of an average museum.

Finally, mention should be made of the fact that a surprising number of the more ingenious and talented forgers simply confess when they learn that their creations are admired and acclaimed and, not incidentally, bringing fantastic prices. There is a desire on the part of nearly all forgers to be recognized as a talent equal to the ancient masters.

FORGERY AND CULTURAL VALUES

Art forgeries are possible because art is, in our culture and times, appreciated for its aesthetic merits and not its function or purpose. Art no longer simply satisfies magical needs or keeps the drafts out of the castle or indicates the special nature of a person by details of costume. Further, art is collectable of and for its own sake. One question to consider is the inordinate emphasis we place upon names and the subsequent value that the work of favored names acquires. Hans Tietze accuses the buying public of abetting the art forger, "By idolizing names instead of worshipping art, ... preferring easy pleasantness to intellectual strain..."[17] In fact the same climate which encourages forgeries of a certain artist's work also explains damaged public regard for the forged artist. Forgery seems to affect the degree of public admiration for an artist, and his idealized image as an inimitable genius suffers; "...Part of the blemish remains with the victimized model."[18]

Are there any positive aspects of fakery and forgery of the fine arts? Scholars agree that shows of this kind and the long-term study of forgeries and fakes as part of the professional responsibility of experts provide invaluable experience and knowledge. All the research done in the course of investigating a suspected forgery adds to the general corpus of knowledge of art. The great German aesthetician, J. W. Goethe (1749-1832), collected counterfeits of ancient coins "...in order to make me more and more appreciative of the originals through comparison with deceptive imitations."[19] It is the current practice in American museums to retain known forgeries and fakes, though not to display them to the general public except as such, for teaching purposes.

ADVICE TO THE BUYER

The prospective collector would wish, unless he were wealthy enough to indulge himself in a very expensive "lesson," to avoid buying a fake or a forgery. Although Ralph F. Colin of the Art Dealers Association of America, Inc., has stated that "...only a very, very small fraction of one per cent of all the art dealings in the United States or in the world, in any one year,...involves fake art,"[20] the prospective buyer, in order to avoid even a mild disappointment, is encouraged to buy from a reputable dealer and simply to study art. Visit museums, attend galleries' exhibitions, read and look at art books. With regard to a specific object, study the history ("provenance") of the object, compare it with others of its type, learn about its purpose in the culture that produced it. The enjoyment of art includes a concomitant responsibility to bring to it an inquiring mind, a willingness to give to the work of art mental energy as well as emotional response.

FOOTNOTE

Finally, one may ask, "If all the experts agreed that this object was beautiful and valuable, why, after its discovery as a fake, is it considered worthless?" The above discussion of the fact that all fakes contain something of their time and, therefore, appeal to their time explains that the faked object will not be timeless, will not appeal, perhaps at all, within a matter of years. It will then be seen more objectively, and its lack of authentic conviction will be apparent. Furthermore, there occurs with the faked object the same kind of public disenchantment expressed toward a legitimate artist whose work is faked. The phenomenon may be explained by the following parable: a person is fine and wonderful, but after he tells you his first lie, he may not be different, but he has changed — very deeply.[21]

Kathryn C. Johnson

NOTES

1. "Art Forgery," **The Metropolitan Museum of Art Bulletin**, XXVI, 6 (Feb. 1968), p. 246.

2. Bernard Denvir, "Faux de Mieux," **Studio International** (July, 1970), p. 57.

3. Hans Tietze, **Genuine and False: copies, imitations, and forgeries** (New York, 1948), pp. 9-10.

4. **Ibid.,** p. 10.

5. Sepp Schüller, **Forgers, Dealers, Experts** (New York, 1960), pp. 14-15.

6. **Ibid.,** p. 80.

7. **Ibid.,** p. 147.

8. Dr. H. Van de Waal, "Forgery as a Stylistic Problem," **Aspects of Art Forgery: papers read by H. Van de Waal, Th. Würtenberger, and W. Froentjes at Institute of Criminal Law and Criminology,** University of Leiden (The Hague, 1962), p. 5, footnote 2.

9. Schüller, **op. cit.,** p. xiii.

10. Tietze, **op. cit.,** p. 13.

11. Clifford Irving, **Fake!** (New York, 1969), p. 232.

12. Tietze, **op. cit.,** p. 55.

13. Schüller, **op. cit.,** p. 95.

14. Dr. P. B. Coremans, **Van Meegeren's Faked Vermeers and de Hooghs** (Amsterdam, 1949), p. 14.

15. Schüller, **op. cit.,** p. 157.

16. Tietze, **op. cit.,** p. 35.

17. **Ibid.,** p. 74.

18. **Ibid.,** p. 73.

19. Schüller, **op. cit.,** pp. xiv-xv.

20. The Metropolitan Museum of Art Bulletin, **op. cit.,** p. 258.

21. **Ibid.,** p. 246.

GIOVANNI BASTIANINI (Italian, 1830-1868)

The name of Giovanni Bastianini, an honest sculptor from Fiesole, has become synonymous with the first world-wide art forgery scandal in history. Bastianini had always been interested in portrait sculpture of the Italian quattrocento which was characterized by a mixture of ideal dignity and uncompromising realism, and after 1848 he produced more or less free imitations of old work of this type. His dealer was Antonio Freppa of Florence who, in 1864, sold to a Paris collector a portrait bust ostensibly of the Florentine Renaissance poet, Hiermus Benivieni. The following year the bust was publicly exhibited, and experts hailed it as an outstanding example of Early Renaissance portrait sculpture, suggesting such possible authors as Donatello, Verrocchio, Desiderio de Settignano, or Antonio Rossellino. The Louvre was so taken with the piece that in 1866 it paid 14,000 francs for "Benivieni" (indicative of the level of enthusiasm is the fact that 46 years earlier the Louvre only offered 6,000 francs for the **Venus de Milo** which had just been discovered).

In the course of an avalanche of publicity about the bust, the dealer Freppa learned of the fraud on the part of the Paris collector who misrepresented Bastianini's piece, and he simply announced the truth. Bastianini himself entered into a newspaper letter debate with French personalities who claimed he could never have created so fine a sculpture. Before he could prove himself, Bastianini died suddenly at the age of 37. It was subsequently learned that other of his works had been misrepresented as old, though his dealer never attempted to sell them as antique originals nor did Bastianini deliberately give them an appearance of age. Further, his prices and the commission asked by Freppa were perfectly in line with prices for contemporary work. Bastianini is regarded historically as a genuine artist whose works were rendered forgeries through lack of discernment by specialists. His figures simply corresponded to the picture that people in the mid-19th century had formed of the Italian Renaissance.

ALCEO DOSSENA (Italian, 1878-1937)

To this day referred to as the "king of forgers," Alceo Dossena was able to assimilate and evoke a wide range of period and personal styles, never actually copying but successfully suggesting work ranging from ancient Greek to Renaissance. Born into a family of artists, Dossena was proficient in all skills though he worked primarily as a sculptor. After a poverty-stricken young adulthood and upon release from military service, Dossena found an eager buyer in Rome for a piece of sculpture that imitated an historic style. Eventually Dossena was established in a Roman studio and, in the employ of two unscrupulous dealers and their contact men, executed sculpture according to their orders for a piece "in the manner of" this or that master. He researched his work, studying examples in museums and art books, and would produce a piece in the style, spirit, and technique of the master specified. Dossena became particularly expert in the manners of Giovanni Pisano, Simone Martini, Vecchietta, Donatello, and Mino da Fiesole.

Publicity occasioned by the detection of forgery in the Renaissance sarcophagus called the "Mino Tomb" revealed to Dossena, perhaps truly for the first time, that he was the dupe of his dealer/managers. He had been badly exploited and underpaid and had apparently thought that the dealers were his sincere friends sending honest orders his way and charging fair prices. Of course, the opposite was true, and it was proved that the dealers had robbed Dossena of millions. Dossena revealed himself to the public through court action against his dealers. Once his identity was known, a vast body of work scattered across Europe and the United States came to be identified as Dossena's. For a time he was a celebrity and had exhibitions of his work at The Metropolitan Museum of Art, among other places. These exhibits revealed how closely he had relied on real prototypes, and, subsequently, his reputation declined. Dossena himself felt this response to be unfair in view of the previous success of his work. Though a thoroughly skilled artisan, Dossena died a pauper, condemned for having been an unwitting forger.

HAN VAN MEEGEREN (Dutch, 1889-1947)

Han van Meegeren, author of paintings supposedly by the 17th-century Dutch painter, Jan Vermeer of Delft, and a number by Vermeer's contemporary, Pieter de Hoogh, is perhaps the most widely known art forger of modern times. Van Meegeren's deception was discovered just after the end of World War II and combined the element of art forgery with the charge of collaboration with the Nazi government. He was originally charged with selling a Dutch national treasure, a supposed Vermeer, to Hermann Goering for the Führer's collection. In an almost predictable bid for fame and revenge upon the Dutch art establishment which he felt had discriminated against him and for which he harbored a consuming hatred, van Meegeren confessed to having forged the painting in question. Further, he claimed to have painted not only the **Christ and the Disciples at Emmaus** which had hung in the Boymans Museum for eight years, verified by all experts as a genuine early Vermeer, but also a number of other "Vermeers" and "de Hooghs."

While in prison awaiting trial van Meegeren painted, before witnesses and with his usual techniques, a **Christ and the Scribes** also in the manner of Vermeer. He used all the proper old pigments, thereby escaping immediate chemical detection, as well as a bakelite-like medium which acquired a hardness identical to paintings hundreds of years old after only a few hours in the oven. Technically he made only a few minor mistakes, but stylistically his prison-painted testimonial to his own powers of deception was not a success. It did not convey the spirit of a Vermeer. What had changed? Authorities agree that van Meegeren considered the **Christ and the Disciples at Emmaus** to be his grand gesture of disdain for the official art world; therefore, it was his best effort. Additionally, he cleverly chose to forge paintings in the style in which Vermeer might have painted at the beginning of his career. There was a gap in scholarly knowledge of Vermeer and, utilizing then current speculations by art historians, van Meegeren simply filled in that gap. Most significantly, however, in view of his initial success was the fact that the world was at war. All fine art was hidden or locked away, and the real Vermeers were not available for comparison with the forgeries. Van Meegeren was convicted of deliberate fraud in that he had painted on old canvas with old colours and brushes, had created signs of great age on his paintings, and, above all, had forged the signatures of Vermeer and de Hoogh. He lived to serve only a few months of his sentence.

ELMYR DE HORY (Hungarian, 20th century)

Elmyr de Hory has the unique distinction of being a forger whose biography was written by another forger of perhaps even greater infamy, Clifford Irving. The two men were neighbors on the Mediterranean island of Ibiza where Elmyr created, in a secret studio, forgeries of paintings and drawings by practically every modern artist of any economic repute. De Hory, like Dossena, sold his fakes through two managers and only managed to retain a small percentage of the profits.

De Hory began as a legitimate artist, having studied with Fernand Leger and been a part of the post World War I Paris art scene. He was attracted to the realm of forgery by an effortless first sale in 1946. A British noblewoman saw a drawing in his studio and remarked, "...that's a Picasso, isn't it?" De Hory did not claim otherwise, sold the drawing to her for 40£ (a little over $100), and later learned that she had sold it for 150£. Until he fell in with his "dealers," de Hory faked and sold paintings and drawings to many European and American galleries and even a few museums, almost always on the pretext of having for financial reasons to part with family treasures. Between 1961 and 1967, however, under the guidance of his dealers, de Hory apparently forged some sixty million dollars' worth of paintings and drawings which were sold to millionaires, art dealers, and museums. A quarter of a million dollars' worth of "Derains," "Dufys," and "Modiglianis" were acquired by the Japanese National Museum of Modern Art in Tokyo. Clifford Irving has estimated that during this period de Hory produced perhaps 1000 items, between 75% and 90% of which remain in collections or museums, ". .unrecognized or undisclosed as fakes."

Detection of de Hory's work is difficult because he forged modern masters, using color slides and reproductions in art books as source material and working in unproblematical contemporary media which are, of course, compatible with that of the original work. Generally, his forgeries were pastiches consisting of overpopularized elements in the work of each artist imitated; they have been characterized as "flabby." Because of the threat to the reputations of his victims posed by publicity, de Hory has never been prosecuted for forgery.

K.C.J.

**CATALOGUE
OF THE
EXHIBITION**

All dimensions are given in inches;
height precedes width precedes depth.

Catalogue entries are arranged chronologically.
References are cited only when pertinent or where
further bibliographical material is provided. A
comprehensive bibliography follows the section of
catalogue entries. Because of the large number
of objects in the exhibition, it has not been possible
to illustrate all of them.

1. Israel Rouchomovski
   Russian, born 1860
   TIARA OF SIATAPHERNES, 1890
   Gold, 6¼ in. h.
   Musee du Louvre, Paris, MNC 2135

One of the single most famous fakes of all time, this Tiara was purchased by the Louvre in 1896 as a work of the 3rd century before Christ, representative of the height of the ancient Greek civilization. While it is not of that period, it today is of singular importance for it shows, in a way no other work of art can, exactly what the taste of the late 19th century was and how they saw antiquities. Like other works in this exhibition, it represents the taste of a generation frozen for us to see, for the Tiara has not changed at all but our way of looking at it has.

The Tiara was made by one Israel Rouchomovski, a Russian silversmith. He claimed that it was done as an exercise, not as a deception, but its history and that of the Odessa goldsmith workshops where many fakes were known to have been produced indicate otherwise. The inscription gives a dedication from the Greek city of Olbia to Siataphernes, a Scythian king, and scenes befitting such a grand gift are engraved and embossed both above and below. The inspiration for the decorations has been shown to come from illustrations which appeared in a book on Greek vase decor written by Ludwig Weisser and published in 1882 and from another similar volume published in Russia in 1889 by Tolstoi and Kondakov.

Doubts had been expressed concerning the piece as soon as it appeared in 1895, but it was vigorously defended by the Louvre until the ultimate coup was delivered when Rouchomovski himself turned up in Paris and claimed authorship. He told how he had worked on it for eight months and how the piece had first been offered to the Imperial Court Museum of Vienna and following that to the British Museum. Both had become suspicious upon noticing that the damaged areas of the Tiara avoided the areas of design with unerring regularity. Rouchomovski, who was a goldsmith of unquestioned talent, could obviously not bear to see his handiwork damaged for the sake of mere authenticity. German experts had further noticed that one of the decorative bands circling the Tiara was in the style of the 5th century B.C. while the garland of grape leaves dates from the 1st century B.C. Rouchomovski had carefully studied the source materials, but he never claimed to be expert in all areas of the field.

2

2. PANEL OF ISTRIAN MARBLE
carved in relief with a mythological scene
Italian, Padua, ca. 1500
Marble, 23¼ x 18¼ in.
Loewi-Robertson, Inc., Los Angeles

The Italian Renaissance was in many ways based upon the classical heritage of both Greece and Rome. The effect of this dependence has been carefully traced in the disciplines of philosophy, science, literature, and the arts. So great was the Italian love for "antique" objects that Renaissance artists were known to produce copies after known forms or even to create their own "antique" objects for the eager collector. This relief falls into the latter category and was even purposely damaged to give it a more convincing look of great age. While the sculptor has attempted to quote correct architectural details, the carving of the bodies is very clumsy and their proportions seem strange even for a provincial piece of late Roman date. This relief is ample proof that the problem of artistic deception is indeed an old one.

3. Fragments of mosaic in Roman style
SCENES FROM POLYGNOTOS' "UNDERWORLD"
    a) TANTALUS AND FURY, 11.6 in. h.
    b) THE DANAIDS, 14.1 in. h.
    c) OKNOS AND THE ASS, 11.4 in. h.
The Art Museum, Princeton University, 203a-c

That these mosaic fragments should preserve complete groups of figures is in itself suspicious. Moreover, examples of work in red and white tesserae are extremely rare. The most conclusive argument against these mosaic scenes as genuine antique works, however, is the fact that the figures are conceived in terms of lines, a factor which connotes translation from a drawing or an engraved original. Ancient mosaics convey three-dimensionality and mass through subtle gradations in tone as well as contour lines. Note, especially, how this lack of variation in tone and complete reliance upon line has created visual confusion in the third scene where Oknos holds the braided rope in front of his torso.

4

5

4. CORINTHIAN VASE AND COVER
Greek, ca. 7th century B.C.
Painted terra cotta, 6⅞ in. h.
The Cleveland Museum of Art, 24.875

This vase represents an extremely interesting type of art forgery. Both sections of the pottery vessel, the vase and the cover, are authentic and date to the 7th century B.C. The painted decoration is, however, a modern addition applied to the vessel to enhance its value. Although the animals and stylized flowers are typical types of decoration, the careless interior detailing and a close observation of the paint used proved the painted decor to be a recent modification.

5. RED FIGURE HYDRIA
In the style of Attic Greece
Painted earthenware, 17¼ in. h.
Museum of Fine Arts, Boston, Res 41:56

This vase of the hydria (water jar) type is painted in the "red figure" style; that is, the objects are the color of unpainted clay, while details and backgrounds are painted black. The decorated zones of Greek pots are those areas where there is the most actual dynamic tension in the vase's structure. In this forgery, whose condition is unbelievably perfect, the figures around the shoulder stand in jerky isolation to one another; in fact, the seated goddess does not actually relate to the rock upon which she is supposedly enthroned. The very stiffness of the brushwork alerts the viewer to a self-consciousness typical of forgeries.

6   7

6. OENOCHOE (wine serving vessel)
   Eastern Mediterranean, 6th-4th or 3rd century B.C.
   Glass (core vessel), 4½ in. h.
   The Corning Museum of Glass, Corning, New York, 50.1.6

7. OENOCHOE (wine serving vessel)
   Probably Spanish, ca. 1880-1900
   Glass (blown vessel), 7 in. h.
   The Corning Museum of Glass, Corning, New York, 59.1.70

Core vessels of glass, dating at least as far back as the XVIIIth Dynasty in Egypt (1570-1349 B.C.) are among the earliest forms of glass hollow ware. These vessels were formed by introducing molten glass around a core mold of sand or clay. Coloured threads of glass were then trailed around the vessel and were "combed" with a sharp instrument to achieve the zig-zag effect which can be seen in this example (Cat. 6).

The modern reproduction of this ancient vessel shape (Cat. 7) was formed by blowing the molten glass into a hollow mold. The rough surfaces of the original, indicating the core-mold technique, may be contrasted with the smoother surfaces of the blown vessel. Note also the exaggerated contours of the modern reproduction in contrast to the well-proportioned original. The late 19th century saw the production of numerous spurious examples of ancient glass as interest in the decorative arts of the classical world increased. The revival of interest in ancient forms and techniques of glass production, however, was important in the genesis of Art Nouveau, as indicated in the works of glass artisans such as Tiffany, who utilized both ancient techniques and forms in his works.

8

9

8. ROMAN-TYPE VASE
    Glass, 6¼ in. h.
    Museum of Fine Arts, Boston, 99.604

9. HELMET
    In the Greek Corinthian Style
    Bronze, 8½ in. h.
    The Cleveland Museum of Art, 26.54

While the shape of this helmet replicates that of original models, the clean condition of the surface and, especially, the inlaid silver decoration prove it to be of recent manufacture. This helmet is one of a group of objects in this country apparently made by the same hand. Since bronze objects lose weight through chemical decomposition over the centuries, the heaviness of the helmet is very peculiar. During this aging process a bronze object will also develop a certain growth of cuprite, a reddish substance formed by the deterioration of the metal; this object exhibits no evidence of cuprite at all.

10

10. HEAD OF TRAJAN
     In the style of a Roman sculptor, 2nd century A.D.
     Marble, 3¾ in. h.
     The Cleveland Museum of Art, 25.468

11. HEAD OF TRAJAN
     Roman, ca. 100 A.D.
     Marble, life size
     Museum, Ostia
     (photograph of object only in exhibition)

The size of this forgery (Cat. 10) is unusually small for a portrait head, the first of many mistakes made by the sculptor. The carving of the piece is "soft" in quality, perhaps an attempt to give it the appearance of age and wear. While the sculptor tried to follow known likenesses of the Emperor (Cat. 11), he miscut the patterns of the hair which are usually consistent in authentic Imperial portraits. Finally, the addition of incised pupils would only be found in Roman portraits of a later date and would not be consistent with a contemporary likeness.

12

13

12. THE GOOD SHEPHERD
In the style of Archaic Greece
Silver, 9½ in. h.
Museum of Fine Arts, Boston, F.74

13. ZEUS
Greek, 1st century B.C.
Gold, 1¾ in. h.
The Minneapolis Institute of Arts, 70.32

Ancient sculptures were frequently cast in precious metals (Cat. 13). Not only did this attest to the devotion of the maker and donor, but they withstood the centuries far better than objects made in more transient materials. The silver GOOD SHEPHERD (Cat. 12), however, is modern. It is made to imitate the archaic style, but its patination has been applied with chemicals to give the appearance of age, and its damaged areas have been eaten away intentionally by acids.

14

15

14. ZEUS
Modern forgery
Bronze, 7 ¼ in. h.
Museum of Fine Arts, Boston, F.57

15. PTOLEMAIC RULER IN GUISE OF HERCULES
Greek, 2nd century B.C.
Bronze, 9 in. h.
The Minneapolis Institute of Arts, 68.81

This forgery (Cat. 14) is probably a cast of an authentic ancient piece. The style is correct, but the scars on the surface are part of the cast, not natural aging. The surface patina, too, is chemically applied, not from natural deterioration.

16

17

16. STATUETTE OF HERAKLES WITH A RAM SKIN
In the general style of Archaic Greece
Bronze, 4¾ x 2 x 2 in.
Conservation Center, Institute of Fine Arts, NYU, New York

17. STATUETTE OF HERCULES WITH A LION SKIN
Etruscan, 4th century B.C.
Bronze, 4¾ in. h.
The Minneapolis Institute of Arts, 63.40

The statuette of Herakles (Cat. 16), the Greek name for Hercules, is most probably a pastiche of Archaic Greek and Etruscan styles. While its torso closely approximates that of the Minneapolis Etruscan piece (Cat. 17), its head, with the typical "archaic smile," was most likely copied from larger archaic sculptures. The forger has also attempted to give this object the look of great age by not casting the legs of the figure, the lack of legs being a misfortune common to many authentic statuettes of this type. An examination of the surface of the fake shows the patination to be modern and chemically produced in contrast to the rich, encrusted surface of the Etruscan original which has aged naturally with the passage of time.

18

18. HEAD OF A DACIAN
In the manner of late Imperial Rome
Porphyry, 20.9 in. h.
Museum of Fine Arts, Boston, 13.2722

The Hellenistic Greeks and Romans paid tribute to the various barbarian tribes that they defeated and assimilated in the course of expanding the "civilized" world. Thus, a portrait of a Dacian (from the land of the Danube), identifiable by his cap, is not unusual. The scholar L. D. Caskey purchased this piece for the Museum of Fine Arts, Boston, in 1913, but in the following year he issued a statement identifying the piece as a forgery. He had in the interim examined many pieces of antique porphyry sculpture and had concluded that the state of preservation of the Boston head was remarkable and rare. The marks, both "mutilation" marks and those at the edges where the piece was supposedly broken from its backing, were unusually fortunate; that is, only the parts that give value were preserved, a saving in material and labor for the forger. Finally, Caskey argued that this piece would, if genuine, be the only example of an antique colossal figure to have a porphyry head. All other known examples had heads worked separately and of a different material, usually white marble. Taken together these arguments point conclusively to a case of modern forgery.

Reference: L. D. Caskey, **"Statement in Regard to the Porphyry Head of a Dacian,"** unpublished manuscript dated October 21, 1914, in possession of Department of Classical Art, Museum of Fine Arts, Boston.

19

20

19. NEO-CLASSIC PORTRAIT OF A MAN
In the style of 3rd-century A.D. Rome
Marble, 11½ x 6¼ in.
Museum of Fine Arts, Boston, Gift of Paul Manheim, 68.769

20. HEAD OF A MAN
Roman, 3rd century A.D.
Marble, 14 in. h.
The Minneapolis Institute of Arts, 62.42

This forged portrait (Cat. 19) was produced between 1770 and 1820 as an item for the then-tourist trade consisting of young scholars and dilettantes engaged in the "Grand Tour." The high point of the Tour was, of course, Rome, mother of Western law, social organization, and culture. Rome in the 3rd century A.D., however, was an unpleasant mixture of bureaucratic power and individualism, of brutality and spirituality as the influence of Eastern mysticism slowly weakened belief in the State. Portraits from the 3rd century A.D. reveal human beings capable of great cruelty, yet haunted by doubts and fears. The Institute's genuine portrait (Cat. 20) rivets the viewer with a questioning gaze. The fake attempts this disquieted look, but the result is simply somewhat annoyed. There is no psychological dimension to the faked portrait.

21. DIANA THE HUNTRESS
In Etruscan style
Terra cotta, 47½ in. h.
The St. Louis Art Museum, 358.52

Much controversy has raged over this sculpture, and there are those who will tell you that the battle is not over yet. In the main it is accepted as a forgery by the master Alceo Dossena, but time was when Dossena's claim to have made it was rejected as grandstanding on his part — a mere attempt to boost his reputation by adding some genuine works to his oeuvre.

Purchased in 1952, it was published on the cover of prestigious ART NEWS for November, 1953. There it was stated: "This 4-foot terra cotta...attributed to an Etruscan artist of ca. 480 B.C....is the only complete female figure of its type and has been named one of the greatest Etruscan finds in history." Assembled from 21 fragments, it received mixed reviews from scholars, some of whom called it representative of the peak of the culture while others immediately cried "fake." Sadly too, it was compared to and vied with the monumental warrior of The Metropolitan Museum in New York (since revealed as a fake as well) for honors as representative of Etruscan style.

Said to have been found in 1872 north of Rome, DIANA appears to have been made right in Rome by Alceo Dossena after the turn of the century. A photograph of the piece, intact, exists, showing it in Dossena's studio in the winter of 1936-37 alongside a piece admittedly fake, now in another museum. The same prestigious ART NEWS in 1962 published an article entitled, "The art of fake Etruscan art," and DIANA was included. She had had her costume shredded by an expert on ancient dress as being stylistically impossible, and other archeologists had demonstrated that she could have existed, not in the 5th century B.C., but only in the 20th.

Dossena's genius lay in his ability to construct his images "in the style of" a period; they were never intended to be historically beyond reproach. DIANA is one of the great examples of what he was capable of. Even today she looks less Etruscan than she did twenty years ago. She has not changed, but our manner of viewing that particular civilization has. She stands as frozen evidence of what "Etruscan" meant to the first quarter of the 20th century.

22

22.   SHAWABTI
In the style of the XVIIIth Dynasty
Limestone, 6¾ in. h.
The Cleveland Museum of Art,
Gift of the John Huntington Art and Polytechnic Trust, 14.591

When examined by Egyptologists, the hieroglyphic inscriptions on the front of this figure were found to be completely wrong. Not only does the inscription make no coherent sense, but some of the characters are complete fabrications of the forger's imagination. This, combined with the fatuous, blank expression of the face, marks this sculpture as an obvious fake.

23.   RELIEF WITH HEAD OF A MAN
In the Egyptian style
Limestone, 5½ x 4¾ in.
The Cleveland Museum of Art, 14.659

The surface of this relief calls the object into question since it exhibits none of the usual signs of age found on authentic Egyptian sculptures of the type. Another mistake made by the forger is the way in which the wig of the man is carved. The exact parallel formation of the lines in the wig should more gracefully reflect the natural fall of the hair.

24

2

24. FRAGMENTS OF A STATUE OF A KING
In the style of the Late period
Green slate, 4 in. h.
The Cleveland Museum of Art,
Purchase, John Huntington Art and Polytechnic Trust, 15.557

The expression of calm, timeless tranquility that marked the sculpture of a people who firmly believed in an eternal life after death is unsuccessfully conveyed in this obvious fake. The crude and shallow carving has led experts to believe that it is a peasant forgery manufactured in the early 20th century.

25. SUNKEN RELIEF OF A PRINCESS
In the style of the Amarna Period (14th century B.C.)
Alabaster, 17 x 13 in.
Acquired as a forgery by The Brooklyn Museum,
Charles Edwin Wilbour Fund, 62.77.3

This head (Cat. 25), in the later Amarna style, was probably copied from a full figure relief of a Princess in Cairo (photograph in exhibition). Information from The Brooklyn Museum indicates that there are no other close parallels.

Reference: **The Brooklyn Museum Annual II. III.** 1960-1962 (The Brooklyn Museum, 1963), p. 110.

26

27

26. RELIEF BLOCK WITH TWO HEADS
In the style of the XIth Dynasty, Egypt
Limestone, 6.2 x 10.6 in.
Acquired as a forgery by The Brooklyn Museum,
Charles Edwin Wilbour Fund, 67.222

27. Photograph of RELIEF OF AMENHOTEP I
Egyptian, XVIIIth Dynasty
Original: Limestone, 6.3 x 9.4 in.
Museum of Fine Arts, Boston,
J. H. and E. A. Payne Fund, 64.1470

The head on the right of the faked relief fragment (Cat. 26) was modeled after this genuine head of Amenhotep I (Cat. 27), second pharaoh of the XVIIIth Dynasty (1570-1314 B.C.) The style of the genuine piece is based on thousands of years of convention but exhibits the typical early New Kingdom qualities of restraint and simplicity; we intuit the intelligent consciousness of this king. In addition to a change in the relief technique, the original is raised while the fake is sunken relief, both faces in the faked fragment wear silly smirks rather than timeless expressions of controlled energy. Subtleties of carving, such as the slight fullness under the eye and around the mouth, are missing in the fake.

Reference: **The Brooklyn Museum Annual IX. 1967-1968** (The Brooklyn Museum), p. 131.

28

29

28. HEAD OF A MAN
Egyptian, Dynasty XXX (?), ca. 350 B.C.
Near black basalt on diabase, 3.4 in. h.
Acquired as a forgery by The Brooklyn Museum,
Charles Edwin Wilbour Fund, 71.10.2

This head has an extremely interesting and intriguing history. It was first seen in 1956 in a dealer's shop in Cairo, a fine, small head whose facial features had been obliterated. In 1966 the same head, identified by its hieroglyphic inscriptions, appeared in a European gallery, but its face had now been recut. This is a perfect example of an authentic object being falsely altered in an attempt to add to its value, a value which is, happily, now an educational one.

Reference: Bernard V. Bothmer, **"The Head That Grew a Face. Notes on a Fine Forgery,"** Miscellanea Wilbouriana 1 (The Brooklyn Museum, 1973), pp. 25-31.

29. CLAY TABLET
In the Assyrian style, ca. 1200-600 B.C.
Baked clay, 4¾ x 2¹⁄₁₆ in.
Museum of Fine Arts, Boston, 21.1352

Clay tablets with cuneiform inscriptions were widely used as official documents in ancient Mesopotamia. In the production of this fake, not only was the wrong type of stylus used, but the inscription itself is meaningless.

30. PORTRAIT OF A WOMAN
After the Faiyum type
Water soluble pigment on panel, 9.5 x 5.7 in.
Acquired as a forgery by The Brooklyn Museum, 51.253.4.

31. PORTRAIT OF A WOMAN
Egyptian
Faiyum type, ca. 2nd century A.D.
Encaustic on panel, 8.5 x 13.6 in.
Academia Moscovia, 1936
(photograph of object only in exhibition)

Faiyum portraits are the direct descendants of the earlier and more elaborate Egyptian mummy portraits which were produced for thousands of years. Like the mummy portraits these were attached to the preserved bodies of the dead as part of the burial ritual. Although original Faiyum portraits (Cat. 31) are often roughly painted, the clumsy, bloated features of this panel (Cat. 30) are very foreign to the Faiyum style. It is also rare to find a head shown in three-quarter view, most of the examples being full-face. This visual evidence is corroborated by simple physical analysis which has shown that the fake was produced with a water soluble paint, rather than the traditional encaustic medium in which the pigments are suspended in hot wax.

32

33

32. Anonymous
Italian, Umbrian School, 15th century
LEAF OF A MISSAL WITH ILLUMINATED INITIAL O
Pen, bistre, gouache, and gilding on parchment, 13$\frac{1}{16}$ x 9$\frac{3}{8}$ in.
The Minneapolis Institute of Arts, 40.14.2

33. "The Spanish Forger"
TWO WOMEN IN A BOAT, ILLUMINATED INITIAL
Pen, ink, gouache, and gilding on parchment, 8$\frac{1}{4}$ x 7$\frac{3}{8}$ in.
The John F. Lewis Collection, M49:11
The Rare Book Department, The Free Library of Philadelphia

The art of embellishing manuscripts with border decorations and miniature paintings had a long and rich tradition in Medieval and Renaissance Europe. Examples of the illuminator's art, such as the page from a missal dated to 15th-century Italy, have long been popular with collectors. Hoping to capitalize on this demand, the so-called "Spanish Forger" produced about 50 known fakes, of which this is an example (Cat. 33). While illuminated initials would have appeared in the context of the whole page, as seen in this example from The Minneapolis Institute of Arts (Cat. 32), they are sometimes found cut from the page, especially in cases where the page itself had been damaged. In this comparison we can see that the "Spanish Forger" has copied his motifs fairly accurately, including the gold leaf background and the two types of floral patterns which decorate the initial. It is, however, in the main scene that his style gives him away. Not only are the figures painted much too broadly and evenly, but there is a curious inconsistency in the angularity of the line used to describe, for example, the hands of the women and those used in the robes of the men. But perhaps the clearest indication of the origin of this work are the faces of the women whose full oval forms, framed by carefully braided and tied hair, are as 19th century as their sweetly pursed, cupid-bow mouths.

Reference: Janet Backhouse, "The Spanish Forger," **The Eric George Millar Bequest of Manuscripts and Drawings, 1967** (London, 1968), pp. 65-71.

34

35

36

34. "The Spanish Forger"
ILLUMINATED PAGE SHOWING THE SIEGE OF A CASTLE
Gouache, pen and ink on vellum, 12¾ x 8¾ in.
The Rare Book Department,
The Free Library of Philadelphia, M75:13

35. "The Spanish Forger"
ILLUMINATED PAGE SHOWING THE TRIUMPHAL
ENTRY OF A FRENCH PRINCELY COUPLE
Gouache, pen and ink on vellum, 13 x 9 in.
The Rare Book Department,
The Free Library of Philadelphia, M75:11

36. ILLUMINATED PAGE WITH A SCENE OF THE CRUCIFIXION
French, ca. 1500
Gouache, pen and ink on vellum, 8¹¹⁄₁₆ x 5⁷⁄₁₆ in.
Special Collections, The University of Minnesota Libraries

The precise detail and exactly painted forms on the illuminated
pages by "The Spanish Forger" (Cat. 34 and 35) lack completely
the richness and ease of the authentic types he was emulating. The
thinly described and repetitive floral borders are especially unconvincing when compared to the rich decorative quality of those on
the authentic page (Cat. 36).

37

38

37. "The Spanish Forger"
THE FLIGHT INTO EGYPT
Gouache, pen and ink, and gilt on vellum, 8¼ x 5¼ in.
The Rare Book Department,
The Free Library of Philadelphia, M31:34

38. Anonymous
French, 15th century
THE NATIVITY,
ILLUMINATED PAGE FROM A BOOK OF HOURS
Gouache, pen and ink, and gilt on vellum
Special Collections, The University of Minnesota Libraries

In this FLIGHT INTO EGYPT "The Spanish Forger" left no margins around the edges of the page in order to give the appearance of having been cut from a larger page of a Book of Hours of the type shown here (Cat. 38). It is interesting to note that in this comparison the surface condition of the forgery is apparently older than that of the 15th-century original. This is because the forger artificially wore and cracked his illumination to give it the look of great age, while the original Book of Hours is in perfect condition, having been carefully preserved since its creation.

39

40

39. MIRROR BACK WITH A SCENE OF A TOURNAMENT
In the style of 14th-century France
Ivory, 3¾ in. diameter
Conservation Center, Institute of Fine Arts, NYU, New York

Scenes of courtly diversions decorate this mirror back which is copied primarily from a 14th-century French model. The ivory surface, especially the faces of the figures, show signs of having been artificially worn down to give the impression of wear and age.

40. MIRROR BACK WITH A SCENE OF A TOURNAMENT
Modern copy of a 14th-century original
Ivory, 5¼ x 4⅞ in.
The Metropolitan Museum of Art, Rogers Fund, 11.93.14

41. MIRROR BACK
THE GOD OF LOVE AT THE SIEGE OF HIS CASTLE
French, first half of the 14th century
Ivory, ca. 5 in. diameter
The Victoria and Albert Museum, London
(photograph of object only in exhibition)

The modern ivory shown here (Cat. 40) is an almost exact copy of a 14th-century French mirror back in the Victoria and Albert Museum, London (Cat. 41). Given the nature of the object, Medieval mirrors were most often decorated with scenes of Love, Youth, and Vanity. The scenes on both mirrors depict Cupid, the God of Love, shown with wings and a bow on the top parapet of his castle "defending" it and four ladies from the knights below. The only major figural change is the replacement of the four lions found on the corners of the original with crouching dragons, another familiar form used on ivories during that period. The carving on the copy is much more exact and even than that of the original, resulting in a finish and proportion which are too polished and facile.

42

42. PLAQUE SHOWING THE DORMITION OF THE VIRGIN
In the Byzantine style
Ivory, 7⅜ x 5⅞ in.
The Metropolitan Museum of Art,
Gift of J. Pierpont Morgan, 17.190.132

43. PLAQUE SHOWING THE DORMITION OF THE VIRGIN
Byzantine, 10th-11th century
Ivory, 5.7 x 4.3 in.
Staatsbibliothek, Munich, Cod. Lat. 4453
(photograph of object only in exhibition)

This plaque (Cat. 42) has been deliberately treated to give it the appearance of great age. In fact it is an almost exact copy of the one in Munich. The only changes made by the forger are the different floral decorations on the two upper corners, the omission of two mourners and the censor above and to the left of the Virgin's head, and the omission of the mourner's head at the upper left. The inscriptions found in the censer of the plaque are also different. In this case the forger borrowed his inscription from another ivory plaque showing the Dormition of the Virgin now in the collection of E. Kofler-Truniger, Lucerne.

44. PLAQUE WITH ST. JOHN THE
    BAPTIST AND FOUR APOSTLES
    Byzantine, 11th century
    Ivory, 9.3 x 5.3 in.
    The Victoria and Albert Museum, London
    (photograph of object only in exhibition)

45. PLAQUE WITH CHRIST AND THE FOUR
    EVANGELISTS
    In the Byzantine style
    Ivory, 7⅝ x 4¼ in.
    The Metropolitan Museum of Art,
    Gift of Edward A. Penniman, 04.25

While the scene on this plaque (Cat. 45) is called Christ and the Four Evangelists, it is directly copied from the plaque showing St. John the Baptist and Four Apostles (St. Philip, St. Stephen, St. Andrew, and St. Thomas) in the collection of the Victoria and Albert Museum (Cat. 44). Instead of using a flat piece of ivory, the forger has carved his figures on a curved piece, a change which somewhat cramps his composition. The five figures and the surrounding floriate designs are all copied quite closely; however, the forger has changed the inscriptions in a very haphazard way. In the process of carving the man who made this copy has also failed to include the pupils of the eyes, adding to the unconvincing and unmoving character of this forgery.

46 47

46. MADONNA AND CHILD
Modern forgery in the style of the late 13th century
Bronze, ca. 9.4 in. h.
Mr. and Mrs. Carroll C. Pratt

47. MADONNA AND CHILD
Modern forgery in the style of the late 13th century
Bronze, 9.4 in. h.
The Art Museum, Princeton University, 55-3272

These sculptures have a common ancestor in an ivory Madonna which resides in the treasury of the Cathedral at Tournai, Belgium. Neither of these bronzes is original; both are fakes and quite possibly one a double fake.

The Princeton piece (Cat. 47) possibly was made as a souvenir of the original, but more likely as a deception. The Pratt group (Cat. 46), however, appears to have been made from the Princeton prototype, faking **it,** and this is doubly off the mark. The disintegration of the style is evident between the two bronzes and would be even more so were the ivory here for comparison.

48. BOOK COVER WITH VIRGIN AND CHILD AND
SYMBOLS OF THE FOUR EVANGELISTS
In the style of mid-12th century, Germany
Copper gilt, cabochons, and porphyry, 12¾ x 9¼ in.
The Metropolitan Museum of Art
Gift of J. Pierpont Morgan, 17.190.405

This piece exhibits a very unconvincing and crude technique of metalwork, beginning with the five main figures and continuing to details of the rough jewel settings. Although no date of manufacture is known, it can probably be ascribed to the late 19th century.

49. CROSS, CORPUS, AND BASE
Base and corpus: French, Mosan, 12th century
Cross: later reconstruction
Copper-gilt with champleve on cross and base, 12 in. h.
The Metropolitan Museum of Art,
Gift of J. Pierpont Morgan, 17.190.341 a-c

This cross, corpus, and base has had a very involved and interesting history which was published by Carmen Gómez-Moreno of The Metropolitan Museum of Art in 1967. While the three pieces were at first believed to have been made as a unit, the article proves that the base and corpus are both authentic, but probably made in different workshops, and the cross is of later construction, manufactured to fit the two original pieces. Both the cross and the base show the symbols and names of the four evangelists; however, on the cross the eagle of St. John has the name of St. Matthew and the winged man of St. Matthew has the name of St. John. Following this incorrect pattern the titulus (the inscription above Christ's head) is of a form never found on pieces of the Mosan school of this period. An examination has further proved that all of the words and names which appear on the cross are incorrectly spelled, the work of someone who obviously was unfamiliar with Medieval lettering and abbreviations.

In stylistic terms the cross has been shown to be too narrow for the corpus, and the downward angle of the arms of the cross is very out of character for pieces of this type. Following this pattern of mistakes the engraved designs on the front and rear of the cross are too regularized and even, a fact that would perhaps point to a Renaissance model but not a Medieval one. The surface condition of the base exhibits all the signs of age and wear that one would expect in a 12th-century object, whereas the cross has a smooth, unpitted surface complete with a superficial patination. Finally, a spectrographic analysis has shown that the metal used for the base and the cross are quite different, indicating varying dates of manufacture.

Reference: C. Gómez-Moreno, "The Mystery of the Eight Evangelists," **The Metropolitan Museum of Art Bulletin,** XXVI, 6 (Feb. 1968), pp. 263-268.

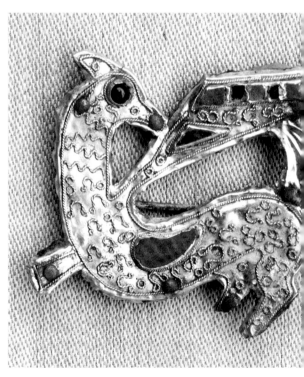

50. PAIR OF FIBULAE
In the 7th-century Frankish style
Bronze, gold, and gemstones, each 2 x 2 in.
The Metropolitan Museum of Art, 17.192.44-45

Fibulae are ornate clasps used to fasten and decorate clothing and normally take the form of a disc or an elegant S-shaped curve. This pair of winged animals is, therefore, quite unusual. Only four others of this type are known, and one of those is also acknowledged as a fake. Besides the discrepancy in subject matter, the application of the gold to the bronze base has been done incorrectly. In authentic pieces the bronze base comes up to form a neat ridge around the outer edge of the form. In this pair the gold sheet is folded over the base. This is not only stylistically wrong, but it also creates a rough edge which could easily catch on the cloth to which it would have been attached.

51

52

51. TRIPTYCH
     Brussels style
     Enamel, 10¼ x 12⅝ in.
     Museum of Fine Arts, Boston, F.13

52. Nardon Penicaud
     French, 16th century
     TRIPTYCH:
        a) THE ANNUNCIATION
        b) THE NATIVITY
        c) THE CORONATION OF THE VIRGIN
     Enamel, side panels each: 5⅛ x 3⅞ in.
                    central panel: 5¾ x 4¾ in.
     The Minneapolis Institute of Arts, Bequest of John R. Van Derlip
     in memory of Ethel Morrison Van Derlip, 35.7.11-13

This is an extremely deceptive work (Cat. 51) and only spectro-graphic analysis finally determined its true colors. Made in Paris around the turn of the century, it is the product of an energetic work-shop which flooded the market for many years. It attempts to dupli-cate the style of the Minneapolis enamels (Cat. 52), but not in the **champleve** style. Its characters have what we have come to detect as "that 19th-century look," but this is the virtue of 20/20 hindsight as much as anything else.

54

55

53. **NIELLO PANEL WITH CRUCIFIXION**
In imitation of Renaissance style
Gilt bronze, 5¹⁵⁄₁₆ x 3⅞ in.
The Art Institute of Chicago,
Buckingham Gothic Room Fund, 1943.86

True niello technique is a branch of the goldsmith's craft, but it was also closely related to the development of line engraving. It involves engraving, or gouging, a linear design into a gold or silver plate and filling in the lines with "niello," a mixture of lead, silver, copper, and sulphur. When the plate is polished, the design appears clearly as black lines on a shiny metal ground.

These panels are imitations of niello work of the Renaissance; their frame, with its classical architectural motifs, is meant to complete the deception.

54. **CANDLESTICK WITH FIGURE MOUNTED ON A LION**
German, 19th century
Bronze, 9 in. h.
Anonymous loan

55. **AQUAMANILE IN THE FORM OF A RIDER ON HORSEBACK**
German, Rhenish, 15th century
Bronze, 13 in. h.
The Minneapolis Institute of Arts, 56.40

Small bronze sculptures were utilized throughout the Medieval period for both religious and secular purposes. Although these objects were used for different functions, we can compare them in general stylistic terms. We should especially note the lack of attention paid to the hair striations on the lion and figure of the 19th-century candlestick (Cat. 54) as opposed to those on the authentic aquamanile (Cat. 55). Although the large head and pug nose of the lion are typical Medieval features, the oriental quality of the face is closer to 19th-century porcelain dogs than it is to original models.

56

57

56. THE MOURNING VIRGIN
from a Crucifixion group
South Netherlandish, ca. 1560-1570
Boxwood, 11¼ in. h.
The Metropolitan Museum of Art, Rogers Fund, 47.31

57. VIRGIN AND CHILD
Flemish
Boxwood, 12¼ in. h.
The Art Institute of Chicago,
Mr. and Mrs. Martin A. Ryerson Collection, 1937.876

This pair of Boxwood sculptures presents an intricate problem of connoisseurship and stylistic analysis. **The Mourning Virgin** (Cat. 56) is an excellent example of Southern Netherlandish sculpture from the late Renaissance. The **Virgin and Child** (Cat. 57) was long thought to have been created in the same area at the same time; it was even a part of the Spitzer Collection, one of the great 19th-century assemblages of Gothic art. It has, however, been recently reattributed to the 19th century on the basis of a reanalysis of its style. A primary point of concern in this reattribution is the manner in which the Virgin's robe has been carved. The robe is defined by a series of short, shallowly carved folds which, combined with the over-all bearing of the body, are more like an Italian or French model than a Southern Netherlandish or Flemish one.

As in the other examples of 19th-century forgeries seen in this exhibition, a further stylistic indication of the object's date may be found through an examination of the face. The spare, intense visage that adds to the moving presence of **The Mourning Virgin** is here replaced by a round, full face whose short, pursed lips give it an over-all sense of sweetness and calm which is so typical of many 19th-century works. Taken in its entirety, this **Virgin and Child** can be seen as the product of a very competent 19th-century sculptor who could not wholly remove himself from the aesthetic preferences which dominated his own era.

58

59

58 a and b. William Smith and Charles Eaton
English, 19th century
PAIR OF BISHOPS, ca. 1850
Lead and copper alloy, each approximately 17 in. h.
Ben Weinreb, London

59. William Smith and Charles Eaton
English, 19th century
MEDALLION, ca. 1850
Lead and copper alloy, 4⅝ in. diameter
Anonymous Loan

"Billie and Charlie," as they were known, duped hundreds of collectors in the last half of the last century, and their works still turn up with surprising regularity.

William Smith and Charles Eaton were illiterate London workmen who displayed a remarkable ability for casting what purported to be Medieval works of art. These they made in large quantities and then buried in building sites along the Thames in London to be "found" and sold.

The medallion (Cat. 59) is typical of what they believed would pass for a pilgrim's medal from the 11th century. The design is pure imagination, however, and the inscription is meaningless in any known language. The bishops (Cat. 58a and b) are also typical, combining as they do originality and naivete. "Billie and Charlies," as they are called, are now collected in their own right.

60. Anonymous (Olof Ohman?)
REPLICA OF THE KENSINGTON RUNE STONE
Plaster cast, 30½ x 15¼ in.
The Minnesota Historical Society Museum

Carving inscriptions in stone has been an accepted method of preserving messages for posterity since the ancient Egyptians left carved hieroglyphs on tablets deep within their tombs. The Vikings, too, carved inscriptions with runes, their alphabet, to document their travels and conquests, and many rune stones have been found in Scandinavia. Very few absolutely authentic stones have been found outside the Vikings' homeland, however, even though many carvings purporting to be original have turned up. Such a curiosity is the so-called Kensington Rune Stone, found in 1898 by farmer Olof Ohman near Kensington, Minnesota.

The inscription reads:
> "Eight Goths and twenty-two Norwegians on an expedition from Vinland to the West. Our camp was on a rocky island a day's march from this stone. One day we went out fishing and when we returned found ten men covered in blood and dead. AVM (Ave Maria) deliver us from evil. Ten men watched by the sea for our ships fourteen days' march away from the island. 1362"

While it is generally accepted that the Vikings had come to the North American continent as early as 986, this stone suggested that today's descendants of the Norsmen could claim their ancestors were in this region more than a century before Columbus stumbled upon the Caribbean.

The 3½-ton version of the stone now at Alexandria notwithstanding, the facts suggest that not only did farmer Ohman find the stone, he made it too. A book on the development of the Swedish language, including extensive references to runes, was found among his effects at his death, and the Minnesota Historical Society found a transcription of the stone's "message" which differs from the stone itself in 15 different instances. This latter document, probably in Ohman's own hand, represents the invention process of the runic inscription rather than a copy of it.

61

61. MADONNA AND CHILD
In the Italo-Byzantine style, ca. late 13th century
Tempera and gilt on panel, 35 x 16½ in.
Courtauld Institute of Art, London

This Madonna and Child closely approximates the two-dimensional decorative style of the late 13th-century Italo-Byzantine period and could well be mistaken for the product of a contemporary workshop. However, a close physical examination reveals that many of the cracks in the gold background have been artificially induced and then filled with a dark pigment. Some of the craquelure even shows evidence of having been painted directly over the gilding to further give it the appearance of age.

62. Imitator of Luca di Tomme (Sienese, active 1356-1399)
20th century Italian copy
CRUCIFIXION
Wood, 13⅞ x 8⅜ in.
The Metropolitan Museum of Art, 25.79

Tempera panels from the Italian quattrocento are characterized by the linear style and expression of pathos that are the heritage of Eastern Christian art. This CRUCIFIXION is a verbatim copy of a panel in Pisa executed in 1366 and was purchased by the Metropolitan Museum in 1925 for study purposes. Although the copy manages to convey a degree of the mood of the original, the imitator has altered its format which includes a triangle with God the Father and the Holy Spirit above the Cross. The imitator has also added, around the edge of the panel, a usually common late Medieval stamp design which, however, does not appear in the original panel.

Further technical examinations revealed that the painting's wooden support is of a pine type not commonly used by Sienese painters, and the fabric covering the panel, under the paint, is not linen as one would expect but rather cotton. Finally, the paint which should be egg tempera is resinous and of modern manufacture.

Reference: Bernard Berenson, **Italian Painters of the Renaissance, Central Italian and Northern Italian Schools** (London, 1968-rev. ed.), Vol. II, fig. 369.

63

64

63. Bernardo Daddi
     Florentine, active ca. 1312-1348
     MADONNA AND CHILD WITH SAINTS
     Tempera type on panel,
     Central panel: $23\frac{3}{10}$ x 10 x $1\frac{7}{8}$ in.
     Right wing: $18\frac{11}{16}$ x 5 x $\frac{7}{8}$ in.
     Left wing: $18\frac{9}{16}$ x $4\frac{15}{16}$ x $\frac{7}{8}$ in.
     The Minneapolis Institute of Arts, 34.20

64. G. F. Ioni
     MADONNA AND CHILD WITH SAINTS
     Oil on panel, 22 x $19\frac{3}{4}$ in.
     Courtauld Institute of Art, London

Ioni, one of the most famous of all forgers, expressed to his age the essence of Italian quattrocento style. He was unable, however, to remove from his style the traits of his own day and his own vision. Thus, while superficially "Renaissance" in appearance, the triptych shown here (Cat. 64) is really purest 19th century. Both paintings have Madonnas as their central theme, and both display Annunciations in their Wing tips. Daddi, however, is expressing awe and otherworldliness while Ioni is merely coy.

65

66

65. G. F. Ioni
In the style of Sano di Pietro (Siena, 1406-1481)
MADONNA AND CHILD WITH ANGELS
Tempera on panel, 19⅞ x 13¹⁵⁄₁₆ in.
The Cleveland Museum of Art, James Parmalee Collection, 40.536

In 1948 this painting was discovered to be by the hand of the famous 19th-century forger G. F. Ioni. It had first aroused the suspicions of scholars because it was in a style much too lyrical and poetic for Sano di Pietro. The faces of the four figures, especially, have a polish and a sense of sharp linearity that bear no relationship to Sano but are known to be common in Ioni's forgeries. A later examination showed that the crackle of the Madonna's blue coat was produced by baking, a method used to produce the artificial cracks in other known works by Ioni. A test cleaning also revealed the wrong color of the green underpaint, a further technical error made by the forger.

66. In the style of Piero della Francesca
PORTRAIT OF A WOMAN
Oil on panel, 12⅜ x 10 in.
Museum of Fine Arts, Boston, F.98

This panel is actually a copy of a known fresco and was taken as an original only three decades ago (New York Herald Tribune, September 29, 1940). The panel is made from the wrong kind of wood, its grain runs vertically rather than horizontally, giving an uncharacteristic type of crackle, and the paint contains cadmium yellow, a modern pigment.

67

68

67. In the style of Sandro Botticelli
PORTRAIT OF A MAN
Oil on panel, 20¼ x 15⅛ in.
D. H. H. Turner, Esq., London

This painting is an exact copy of Botticelli's "Portrait of a Man with a Medal" in the Uffizi, Florence, with two changes to transform it into a "different" work. The first is the metamorphosis of the round medal into an open book, an angular object which does not correspond to the circular space left by the hands. The second is the obliteration of the background, a panoramic landscape in the original painting, and its replacement by a far less taxing plain ground.

Reference: Van Marle, **The Italian Schools of Painting**, Vol. XII (The Hague, 1931), fig. 17.

68. In the style of Sandro Botticelli
MADONNA AND CHILD
Oil on panel, 31 x 18 in.
Courtauld Institute of Art, London

This forger has very skillfully executed Botticelli's style using faces, garments, and body forms that are very similar to those in a number of the master's works but are not copied exactly from any of them. A careful examination of Botticelli's oeuvre reveals a number of paintings whose figures and compositions bear strong resemblances to those in the fake, and it is probable that in combination they served as the prototypes for this work.

The heads of both the Madonna and the baby are very close to those used in the **Madonna della Melagrana** and the **S. Barnaba Altarpiece,** both in the Uffizi in Florence. They would seem to have been strongly influenced by these two works taken together. The architectural motif of the archway behind the figures is a very typical Renaissance device but was used by Botticelli only in one work: the figure of **Fortitude,** also in the Uffizi.

This forgery is excellent and, because it copies no specific elements of known Botticelli paintings, would be difficult to recognize as a fake were it not that scientific analysis revealed both the panel and the pigments to be 19th century.

Reference: Van Marle, **The Italian Schools of Painting**, Vol. XII (The Hague, 1931), figs. 50 and 79.

70

69. Copy after Raphael
ST. SEBASTIAN
Oil on panel, 18⅜ x 14½ in.
Museum of Fine Arts, Boston, F.96

Originally attributed to Raphael himself, this painting was later given to Raphael's master, Perugino. Neither is correct, as it is copied after a known Raphael. The panel is taken from an old piece of furniture and thus has the authentic appearance of age. At the earliest it was done at the end of the 18th century when cobalt blue was discovered, for that pigment appears here. Further proof of its fraudulent intent is the fact that the cracks which normally adorn the surface of such paintings have here been painted on.

70. MADONNA AND CHILD
19th-century copy after Bernardino Luini (ca. 1475-after 1532)
Oil on poplar panel, 34⁵⁄₁₆ x 26⅝ in.
The Cleveland Museum of Art,
Bequest of Mrs. Francis F. Prentiss, 44.87

Bernardino Luini was one of the principal followers of Leonardo da Vinci, arriving at a compromise between Leonardo's mysterious softness and the penchant for naturalism characteristic of northern Italian painting. This painting is a 19th-century student copy of a painting in the collection of the Museo di Capodimonte in Naples though for a time it was thought to have been a copy by Luini himself. Although it was created legitimately in the time-honored academic tradition of art education through emulation of the masters, it was later misrepresented as an original.

A

B

C

71

71. Anonymous
Italian, 17th century
MONA LISA, AFTER LEONARDO DA VINCI
Oil on canvas, 32.3 x 25.2 in.
Musée du Louvre, Paris, Inv. MNR 265

Certainly one of the most copied and most influential paintings in the history of art, Leonardo's MONA LISA still retains her aura of mystery and enigma. Little is known about the original painting save a few contemporary references. It is known that between 1500 and 1507 Leonardo painted a portrait of the wife of one Francesco di Bartolomeo del Giocondo, a Florentine merchant. This portrait, with its subtle modelling, its complex composition, and its enigmatic expression, has become a model on which not only countless Renaissance portraits were based, but those up to and including our own day. The painting was greatly prized by Leonardo's contemporaries, and Francis I, King of France, bought it for his collection, paying 4000 scudi or the equivalent of 12 tons of silver.

Copied by students and followers of Leonardo, there are even other versions said to be by the master's hand. One in the Pulitzer collection in London claims, in fact, to be the original after which the Louvre version was made. This situation is further complicated by the fact that the Louvre picture was stolen in 1911, and forgeries were made of it during its absence. To this day there are some adherents to the theory that the Louvre never did recover the proper version.

Shown here is a copy by an anonymous artist of the 17th century who, while able to do a workmanlike job, could not, as others could not, capture the rare essence of the human condition embodied in the now almost cliché smile. It is a countenance neither animated nor at rest and suggests rather the stirrings of that which is unpaintable — the soul.

eonardo da Vinci, MONA LISA,
lusée du Louvre

h. Chasseriau, MONA LISA
fter Leonardo da Vinci

nonymous PORTRAIT OF LADY
spired by MONA LISA,
lusée de Tours

nonymous 16th-century copy
f MONA LISA, Musée de Tours

72

73

72. Francesco Ubertini called Bacchiacca
Italian, 1495-1557
Poster of PORTRAIT OF A LADY
Original: Oil on panel, 40½ x 31½ in.
Property of Fine Arts Corporation (J. Paul Getty), G-61

73. Imitator of Bacchiacca
Italian, 19th century
PORTRAIT OF A LADY
Oil on canvas, 40¼ x 31 in. (sight)
Frescobaldi Collection, Florence

Those who saw the magnificent exhibition, The J. Paul Getty Collection, in Minneapolis in the summer of 1972 will no doubt recall the hauntingly beautiful portrait which graced the poster of the show (Cat. 72). This painting was for many years in an English private collection and not widely known to the world at large. The Getty painting is the original from which the copy (Cat. 73) was made in the early 19th century. A line for line copy, its intent was to deceive. An ancestor of its present owners had it copied so that he could sell the real painting and not have his family know that he was in need. For two generations after the substitution his heirs thought they owned the original only to discover their error when, in 1967, Getty bought his painting at public auction in London.

The copyist has done a far better than average job in retaining the character of the original, but he was unable to achieve the wistful expression of the sitter which is purest 16th century. The two ladies are sisters, even twins, but not the same. Note too that the copyist has given his sitter a slightly different musical score.

74. THE ANNUNCIATION
In the early 15th-century Flemish style
Oil on panel, 9 x 6½ in.
D. H. H. Turner, Esq., London

This painting has purported to be by the famous early 15th-century Flemish master Jan van Eyck. The work in no way reveals any similarity to Van Eyck's exquisite, delicate style and scrupulously observant handling of the minute details of reality. Technically it falls far short of his carefully built up and precisely articulated surfaces. Because it also fails to correspond to any of his known compositions of the Annunciation, it would seem that this is a deliberate misattribution after the fact, rather than a forgery. The painting is probably the work of a minor artist of Van Eyck's period or a little earlier.

75. In the style of Pieter Brueghel the Elder (ca. 1525/30-1569)
RELIGIOUS PROCESSION WITH HOLY IMAGES
Oil, 10¾ x 16⅞ in. (sight)
Courtauld Institute of Art, London

There are a number of compositional characteristics in this forgery that indicate immediately that it is not from Brueghel's hand. In all his paintings utilizing a group of figures, Brueghel's treatment of space is extremely broad or even panoramic. His strongest compositional tendency, whether in landscapes or indoor scenes, is towards spatial depth with strong diagonals moving the eye briskly from foreground to distant background. This is not an arbitrary device, but a visual exponent of Brueghel's philosophy of life: that all individuals' actions, and indeed all human events, are but a small and insignificant part of the totality of nature and the universe.

The space of this painting is far too shallow and shut in. It has no depth and its movement is basically horizontal and without a visible goal. In its stage-like quality it violates the most obvious visual aspect of a true Brueghel work. There is also no example in Brueghel's oeuvre of an architectural repoussoir element — that is, a partially revealed object in the foreground used to establish the spatial depth that should lie beyond. The roof fragment used here is not only alien to Brueghel but is out of place in such a shallow composition. In general, this forgery looks more like a detail of a larger work by Brueghel, like a small piece of a complex painting. The artist, in attempting to establish it as a separate and complete work, has revealed a lack of understanding of the most elementary characteristics of Brueghel's art.

76

B

C

D

76. In the style of Barthel Bruyn (1493-1553/6)
German, 19th century
PORTRAIT OF A MAN
Oil on panel, 10¼ x 8½ in.
Doerner-Institut, Munich

The pastiche is one of the cleverest of frauds because it takes select parts of genuine pictures and combines them in an inventive manner. It thus avoids the risk of detection that a line-for-line copy does, as there is no "original" with which it can be compared. Only after laborious searching do the parts which the pasticheur used turn up.

In the example shown here we see a portrait rather convincingly claiming to be by Barthel Bruyn. It is painted on panel and has other traits that a genuine 16th-century portrait would have. The fact is that the face has been "lifted" from a portrait in Berlin by Memling (B), the hat from a portrait by Bruyn in Frankfurt (C), and the hand holding the coin is found in another Memling now hanging in Antwerp (D).

All of the above notwithstanding, chemical analysis of the pigments used in the painting indicates colors of modern manufacture. Ultramarine, for example, was not invented until 1830, and any painting purporting to be before that date should not be so bold as to use it.

77

78

77. In the style of the Master of Bruges
PORTRAIT OF AN OLD WOMAN
Oil on wood, 8 x 6⅜ in.
Museum of Fine Arts, Boston, F.37

Cleverly constructed as a deception, this PORTRAIT OF AN OLD WOMAN imitates the style of an anonymous master who is known only by the name of the city where he painted. By avoiding the major masters perhaps the faker thought he would avoid detection. He even went to the trouble of carving the frame and panel out of the same piece of wood (the frame is now largely cut away). Scientific investigation revealed the presence of two modern pigments, however, notably Prussian blue and zinc white, neither of which was known at the time this panel was supposed to have been painted.

78. In the style of Rembrandt Harmensz. van Rijn
REMBRANDT'S SON TITUS
Oil on canvas, 21 x 17 in.
The Detroit Institute of Arts, 53.351

The records first mention this painting as having been sold in Paris in 1895. All major sources now concur that it is a later imitation which seems to bear no clear relationship to any authentic portrait of Titus.

Reference: A Bredius, **Rembrandt: The Complete Edition of the Paintings,** revised by H. Gerson (London, 1969), Cat. 127.

79

79. In the style of Rembrandt Harmensz. van Rijn
MAN WITH A BEARD
Oil on canvas, 28⅞ x 25¼ in.
False signature and date: Rembrandt/F. 1665
The Metropolitan Museum of Art,
Gift of Henry G. Marquand, 89.15.3

While long thought to be authentic, the MAN WITH A BEARD was justly removed from Rembrandt's list of works by K. Bauch who thought it to be an 18th-century English imitation. The painting was engraved by W. Ballie in 1764, so it was at least painted before that date. While the look is superficially that of Rembrandt, the rigid frontality of the pose, the flatness of the body, and the lack of personality in the face all suggest a later imitation.

Reference: K. Bauch, **Rembrandt Gemälde** (Berlin, 1966), p. 48.

80. In the style of Rembrandt van Rijn
SELF-PORTRAIT
Oil on canvas, 27⅝ x 22¼ in.
Museum of Fine Arts, Boston, F.95

Taken very directly from two known, late Rembrandt portraits, this rather unconvincing work retreats behind its surface rather than glowing from within. A first impression would be that this might be an original much in need of a cleaning, but only the buyer of it would get that.

81

81. Imitator of Vermeer
Dutch (?)
YOUNG WOMAN READING
Oil on canvas, 7¾ x 5¾ in.
The Metropolitan Museum of Art,
The Jules S. Bache Collection, 49.7.40

This painting is a pastiche. The head and attitude of the woman are derived, though reversed, from Vermeer's "Lady Reading a Letter" in Dresden, while the painting in the background is taken from the "Love Letter" in the Rijksmuseum. In all of Vermeer's oeuvre there is no chair with arms and posts turned in the manner shown here. Though the imitator has added thick dabs of paint to the woman's shoulder and coiffure, creamy impasto textures being characteristic of Vermeer's anonymous portraits, the chief element enabling the viewer to see this painting as a fake is the treatment of space. Vermeer's portraits deal with either intimate, crowded space, the subject very close, or fairly deep rooms, the subject distant and seen objectively. This space is shallow and unevocative of any kind of mood.

82

83

84

82. Han van Meegeren
Dutch, 1889-1947
THE LETTER, in the manner of Vermeer
Oil on canvas, 21⅝ x 18½ in. (sight)
Rijksmuseum, Amsterdam

83. Han van Meegeren
Dutch, 1889-1947
PORTRAIT OF A LADY, in the manner of Ter Borch
Oil on canvas, 24½ x 18½ in.
Yale University Art Gallery, New Haven, Connecticut

84. Han van Meegeren
Dutch, 1889-1947
PORTRAIT OF A BURGHER, in the manner of Ter Borch
Oil on canvas, 11¼ x 9 in. (sight)
Rijksmuseum, Amsterdam

Han van Meegeren was clearly one of the most remarkable forgers of all time. He assiduously studied the style and techniques of the Dutch 17th-century masters he imitated and then produced works which, while ultimately unmasked, were highly deceptive.

In the examples shown here we can see that the resinous paints he employed (and made) yield a surface remarkably akin to that expected of originals and his method of rolling his canvases produced a transfer of the craquelure from the old support to the new. He was, however, unable in the final analysis to shed his own 20th-century origins, and his subjects have faces and expressions curiously of our times and not of the 1600s. His "Vermeers" (Cat. 82) are too coarse and lack the necessary lady-like qualities, his "Ter Borchs" (Cat. 83 and 84) too timid and not filled with a pre-possessing self-confidence.

86

85. In the style of Albert Cuyp (1620-1691)
ON THE ICE, probably 18th century
Oil on panel, 23½ x 32¾ in.
Bayerischen Staatsgemäldesammlungen, Munich

The 18th century was very much smitten with the style of painting common in the Netherlands in the century before. While paintings were often copied out of purest respect, they later lost their respectable character and acquired false signatures.

Such is the case here. A very deceptive painting fully signed at the lower right "A. Cuyp," it was submitted to chemical analysis. The results showed that there are large areas using what is called Berlin or Prussian Blue. This pigment was not known until 1704, 13 years after Cuyp's death, and was not in common usage for another two decades. Thus, while one can prove that it is impossible for Cuyp to have painted this panel, science can not prove who did. It is reasonable to assume that a very talented hand was at work here and, in all probability, one that originally did not intend to deceive.

86. Gerbrand Ban
Dutch, 1613-ca. 1652
PORTRAIT OF A MAN, 1651 (formerly called "Henry VIII")
Oil on panel, 47⅛ x 34¾ in.
Walker Art Center, Minneapolis, X. 2136

The left half of this painting represents what was once thought to be a portrait of Henry VIII of England by his court painter, Hans Holbein the Younger. 20th-century scholarship attributed it to a later 16th-century follower of Holbein and even later followers. Finally, in 1945, Mr. and Mrs. Julius Held, in the course of cleaning and studying the portrait, discovered the picture of a Dutch burgher underneath, seen on the right half. Infra-red photographs revealed the signature of Gerbrand Ban and the date, and the decision was made to leave the painting half-cleaned as an educational exhibit.

As a forgery it is of a rather unique type — that is, not a complete overpainting of an old canvas or panel, not a complete invention. It is, rather, the "dressing up" in the costume of a more ancient time of a perfectly respectable portrait. The majority of the painting, then, dates from the 17th century with later additions. The figure must have been clothed in his Tudor garments some time during the 19th century or earlier, as the painting was exhibited at Manchester's Royal House of Tudor City in 1895.

87

8

89

87. Dirck van Baburen
Dutch, active 1611-d. 1624
THE PROCURESS, 1622
Oil on canvas, 39¾ x 42¼ in.
Museum of Fine Arts, Boston, Maria T. B. Hopkins Fund, 50.2721

88. Hans van Meegeren
Dutch, 1889-1947
THE PROCURESS, after Baburen, ca. 1940
Oil on canvas, 30 x 38 in.
Courtauld Institute of Art, London

89. Anonymous
Dutch, 17th century
THE PROCURESS, after Baburen
Oil on canvas, 39.4 x 37.8 in.
Rijksmuseum, Amsterdam, No. 394

Dirck van Baburen, artist of the Utrecht school, painted in the Netherlands in the Italianate or Caravaggesque style. Strong contrasts of light and shade distinguish his works, and many of his paintings are night or candlelight scenes as was also the fashion among Baburen's contemporaries, Honthorst and Terbrugghen. These three paintings, shown together here for the first time, are respectively an original Baburen, a forgery after Baburen, and a painting dating from the 17th century which for many years was taken to be the original.

The Boston picture (Cat. 87) was "lost" for many years and finally turned up at auction in London in February, 1949 as a Honthorst. It was very dirty, having accumulated centuries of grime, and the misattribution was perhaps only wishful thinking. The dealer who bought the painting, however, saw that there was the trace of a signature on the bottom of the lute, and after cleaning the correct name was once again returned to the painting. Comparison with the Rijksmuseum painting (Cat. 89) clearly indicated that, while contemporary with each other, the two works were by different artists. The most notable difference, aside from the rather more harsh quality of the copy, is that the copy is cut down on the right, and the Procuress herself is given a less prominent position. While more centrally balanced, the emphasis was shifted from the madam to the music.

What is especially interesting about the Baburen is the fact that Vermeer once apparently owned the Boston picture, as it hangs on the wall in the background of two of his paintings. It has been shown that, indeed, it is the Boston picture and not the Amsterdam one and thus arises a curiosity. Van Meegeren's PROCURESS (Cat. 88) was forged before the Boston picture reappeared, but his proportions correspond to it rather than to the Amsterdam painting which he might have been able to have seen. Thus, one can only assume that Van Meegeren cleverly recreated the painting from a photograph of the Vermeer now in the National Gallery, London and tried to pass his work off as the "lost" painting before it actually reappeared. The condition of the Courtauld Van Meegeren is consistent with a canvas which had undergone many years of abuse, but, of course, it is the youngest of them all.

90. In the style of El Greco
ST. PETER
Oil on canvas, 28.7 x 22.6 in.
Doerner-Institut, Munich

Similar in style and concept to the full-length **St. Peter** in the Sacristy of the Escorial, Madrid, suspicions about this painting were raised when surface cleaning revealed easily soluble pigments. Chemical testing suggested a modern origin, but x-rays positively identified the **St. John** underneath. A small "window" was opened to the portrait below yielding the dramatically startling appearance we see today.

Reference: Harold E. Wethey, **El Greco and his School** (Princeton, 1962), Vol. I, Cat. No. 274.

91. In the style of El Greco
PORTRAIT OF A MAN
Oil on canvas, 20 x 17½ in.
The Brooklyn Museum, Gift of the Executors
of the Michael Friedsam Estate, 32.813

This portrait is an exact copy of an authentic painting by El Greco in the Prado Museum, Madrid. An X-ray examination of the work revealed a large fragment of drapery in the lower right-hand corner which had nothing to do with the painting on the surface of the canvas. Interpretation of the X-ray indicated that the portrait purportedly by El Greco was painted over a cut-down piece of a genuinely old painting. Further examinations have shown the surface paint to be relatively modern.

Reference: Oxford University Press, **The Paintings of El Greco** (New York, 1938), Cat. 106.

92. In the style of Francisco de Zurbarán
STILL LIFE
Oil on canvas, 21½ x 51 in.
The St. Louis Art Museum, 114.42

93. Francisco de Zurbarán
Spanish, 1598-1664
Color reproduction of STILL LIFE
Original: Oil on canvas, 23⅝ x 41⅛ in.
Norton Simon Foundation

In the history of art it is not uncommon to find more than one version of a painting. Artists often copied their own works if a sufficiently attractive offer were made, or, more often, the studio of an artist was set to copying both for the instructional purposes of the students and for the purposes that photography serves today.

This painting by an unknown forger (Cat. 92) has been much debated over the years by art historians, but the general consensus lately has been that it was not by Zurbarán's hand. Some suggested that both this and the version now in the Norton Simon Collection (Cat. 93) were by the master himself, but more opted for the Simon version's being authentic and the St. Louis picture's being either by the artist's son, Juan or, worse, a copy after the artist's lifetime. The truth may now be told.

Bothered by the unsettled matter, the authorities at The St. Louis Art Museum submitted the painting to scientific examination. Conservator Clements Robertson discovered that the paint employed was of a resinous nature, not to be expected in paintings of the 17th century. Further he determined that the material found in the cracks of the painting was not the accumulation of centuries of dirt and aged varnish, but rather graphite of the type found in black paint, thinned. Finally, a spectroscopic examination of the paint itself revealed cadmium sulphide yellow and chromium oxide green, both of them pigments which were not invented until nearly two hundred years after Zurbarán's death. This, then, was not a studio copy; it was a forgery.

X-ray examination revealed another painting beneath, and careful and selective removal of the "Zurbarán" yielded the fascinating state shown here. The canvas is indeed old, but the **Still Life** dates from the 19th century. Compared with the reproduction of the original, one can see that the forger was extraordinarily skilled. His composition is slightly cut down and his colors are moderately different, but his sensitivity to the artist's original is, in general, remarkable. Small wonder that such a deception survived unchallenged for so long a time. The major difference between the two paintings is not in substance but in essence. The original is basically a religious painting and, as such, is filled with a curious Spanish mysticism. The forgery is little more than a still life.

92

93

94. Workshop of Charles le Brun
THE HOLY FAMILY IN EGYPT or THE EDUCATION
OF CHRIST, ca. 1655-1656
Oil on canvas, 20 x 16½ in.
Menil Foundation, Houston

95. Charles Le Brun
French, 1619-1690
THE HOLY FAMILY IN EGYPT (Le Christ Lisant), ca. 1655-1656
Oil type on fabric, 20⅜ x 16⅝ in.
Initialed, lower right on step: CLBF
The Minneapolis Institute of Arts, 65.40

This pair of fine paintings is a perfect example of the Baroque tradition of an artist's making more than one version of a popular picture. Although of the two only the Minneapolis picture (Cat. 95) bears the initials of the artist, both are considered to be mainly by the hand of the master. The other major difference besides the initials is the Hebrew text which is found on the scrolls of the Minneapolis painting, but not on the one from Houston (Cat. 94). Our version was engraved in the late 17th century by G. Rousselet (Les Oeuvres de Charles Le Brun d'apres les gravures de son temps) and shows the Hebrew characters but not the initialed signature. Two other versions of this scene are known to exist, one in the Fitzwilliam Museum, Cambridge, entitled THE HOLY FAMILY, and another in the Louvre Museum, Paris, entitled LE CHRIST LISANT. This should stand as an example of the fact that several versions of the same painting need not imply a case of forgery.

96. Jean Honoré Fragonard
French, 1732-1806
PORTRAIT OF A YOUNG LADY,
MLLE MARIE-CATHERINE COLOMBE
Oil on canvas, 18⅛ x 14¹⁵⁄₁₆ in.
The Brooklyn Museum, lent by the heirs
of Mrs. Florence E. Dickerman, L69.5.5

97. Imitator of J. H. Fragonard
20th century
PORTRAIT OF A YOUNG LADY
Oil on canvas, 18⅛ x 15¼ in.
The Brooklyn Museum, lent by the heirs
of Mrs. Florence E. Dickerman, L69.21

Mrs. Watson Dickerman, deciding she wished to dispose of her painting by Fragonard, turned it over to an art dealer named Anthony Seaton in New York. Seaton informed Mrs. Dickerman that the lovely 18th-century portrait would fetch a good price and that she must only be patient.

Some months later the painting remained unsold, and Mrs. Dickerman requested its return. Once back in her house, however, Mrs. Dickerman noticed that the painting had not only seemingly lost some of the original charm which she remembered but had acquired a rather noticeable odor of linseed oil. The dealer, when questioned, said he had merely cleaned the painting to facilitate sale and the smell would go soon.

Sooner than that Mrs. Dickerman went to Sheldon Keck, then restorer for The Brooklyn Museum, who pronounced her Fragonard a copy after the original and further produced a dealer who claimed to have bought the real Fragonard from — Anthony Seaton.

Seaton, who had had the copy made and hastily aged, was promptly arrested and shortly thereafter committed suicide in his cell. His copy (Cat. 97), which bears familial resemblance to Mlle Colombe, is only a first cousin and not a twin.

The original young lady (Cat. 96) has a shy and retiring grace, a softness and a charm which, first of all, only existed in those measures in 18th-century France and, secondly, only flowed so freely off the brush of Fragonard himself. The copy possesses a wooden chin, a spilled on, not silken, dress, and a mouth which barks, not beckons. Nonetheless, the viewer should ask himself if, without benefit of comparison, his visual memory would have been as acute as the owner's.

98

LORENZO DE' MEDICI

99

98. In the style of Francesco di Simone (15th-century Italian)
MADONNA AND CHILD
Marble, 37 x 29¾ in.
Museum of Fine Arts, Boston, Res 17.1467

This very effective forgery dates from the era of Bastianini, if not from his own hand. The top of the slab appears to have been broken intentionally for effect and carefully avoids the areas of the composition. The hand of St. John which rests on the shoulder of the Christ Child is vastly out of proportion, and the drilling of the eyes in all three of the figures is not in keeping with the style it purports to be. If original, one would expect to possibly find traces of color on the piece, but there are none and never appear to have been any.

99. Once attributed to Andrea del Verrocchio
19th century
BUST OF LORENZO DE' MEDICI
Terra cotta, 21¾ in. h.
Museum of Fine Arts, Boston, 17.1477

This bust is one of many 19th-century portraits which evoked the naturalism esteemed at that time as the most prominent character-istic of Renaissance sculpture. At the same time the figure is idealized but lacks the haughtiness displayed by a real portrait bust by Verrocchio of Giuliano de' Medici, Lorenzo's brother. This emptiness is especially apparent around the eyes. Although the motif of the winged, grimacing masks on the figure's armour is borrowed from Verrocchio, the details of costume, as well as the hair, are handled rather too broadly.

100. Once attributed to Leonardo da Vinci
BUST OF FLORA
Wax, 19½ in. h.
Anonymous loan

In the first part of the century a bust, of which this is a copy, was purchased as being by Leonardo da Vinci. It was subsequently "proven" that the bust was made by one Richard Cockle Lucas on the evidence of his son's admission that his father had made it in imitation of the 16th century. The scandal surrounding this revelation rocked the art world.

Today, however, the bust has been reattributed, not to Leonardo, but to an anonymous sculptor indeed of Leonardo's school, and the claim of Lucas has been discarded.

101. Giovanni Bastianini
Italian, 1830-1868
BUST OF A LADY
Marble, 21½ in. h.
Anonymous loan

This statue, unlike other works by Bastianini, was never very deceptive. For many years it sat as a decoration in the home of a private collector who knew of its origins in the 19th century. Placed, however, on top of a Renaissance commode it gave a very appealing suggestion of antiquity.

102

102. Giovanni Bastianini
Italian, 1830-1868
MADONNA AND CHILD, style of Padua, late 15th century
Marble, 22¼ x 15 in.
Museum of Fine Arts, Boston, Res 17.1472

By his own admission Bastianini made numerous sculptures "in the manner of" the artists of the Italian Renaissance. He said he was merely enamoured of their works and not attempting to create forgeries; that was the doing of the unscrupulous dealers with whom he traded. He was probably right.

But forgeries they did become, for Bastianini was able to do what few sculptors can: he rid himself of almost all of the vestiges of his own time and immersed himself in the style that he was evoking. Very few of his works are copies. They are his original inventions. This MADONNA AND CHILD looks less 15th century than 19th today, but we must not lose sight of the fact that it is over a hundred years old and what looked "Paduan" then looks less so now.

103. Martin Schongauer
German, ca. 1450-1491
CHRIST BEFORE THE HIGH PRIEST, ca. 1480
Engraving, 6⅜ x 4½ in.
The Minneapolis Institute of Arts, Gift of Herschel V. Jones, 1926

104. Adriaen Huybrechts
Flemish, died after 1614
CHRIST BEFORE THE HIGH PRIEST, 1584
Engraving in reverse, 6⅛ x 4⅛ in.
Martin Gordon, New York

Of the twelve plates in Schongauer's Passion series, this is number three (Cat. 103). Many sets of copies were made, most out of admiration and scarcity rather than malice. Huybrechts signed and dated only the first plate of his copy of the series (Cat. 104), but anyone familiar with the originals would not be confused. The copies are weak and lifeless, not to mention being in reverse, especially in light of the original shown here since it is recognized as one of the finest impressions in the world.

105. Martin Schongauer
German, ca. 1450-1491
CHRIST TAKEN CAPTIVE, ca. 1480
Engraving, 6⁷⁄₁₆ x 4⁹⁄₁₆ in.
The Minneapolis Institute of Arts, Gift of Herschel V. Jones, 1926

106. Adriaen Huybrechts
Flemish, died after 1614
CHRIST TAKEN CAPTIVE, 1584
Engraving, 6⅛ x 4⅛ in.
Martin Gordon, New York

These prints are similar to the preceding comparison (Cat. 103 and 104) only not reversed. The fake (Cat. 106) could be passed off as an original Schongauer to a naive buyer. It is a very thin impression, however, and lacks any signature. The identifying characteristic of the copy is the raised, armoured glove in the left background which lacks the rivets appearing in the original at the wrist.

107. Copy after Leyden (C. Metz?)
JOSEPH INTERPRETING HIS DREAMS TO JACOB
Engraving, 5¼ x 6¾ in.
Martin Gordon, New York

108. Lucas van Leyden
Dutch, 1494-1533
JOSEPH INTERPRETING HIS DREAMS TO JACOB, 1512
Engraving, 5 x 6⁹⁄₁₆ in.
The Minneapolis Institute of Arts, Gift of Herschel V. Jones, 1926

The copy (Cat. 107) lacks inspiration and originality. Copying allows the artist no freedom as he slavishly reproduces another master's lines. The stiffness of the line in the copy is as evident as the different colors of the paper.

109. Zoan Andrea
Italian, active 1475-1505
JUDITH WITH THE HEAD OF HOLOFERNES
Engraving, 11¾ x 8⅝ in.
The Minneapolis Institute of Arts,
Gift of Herschel V. Jones, 1926

110. Zoan Andrea
Italian, active 1475-1505
JUDITH WITH THE HEAD OF HOLOFERNES
Engraving, 12¾ x 9⅞ in.
The Minneapolis Institute of Arts,
Gift of Mr. and Mrs. Donald S. Winston, P.71.187

These are both impressions of the same print, but in vastly differing conditions. So rare are early Italian engravings that the version without the ball on top of the tent (Cat. 109) is in actuality only a print in a damaged state which has been "repaired," although incompletely.

Done after Mantegna, in reverse, the edges of the repaired Andrea were evidently in such poor condition that the restorer has completely silhouetted the print to preserve only the printed portions of the page. The repairs in pen, watercolor, and new paper have aged since their creation and are far more evident now than when first done.

111

11.

111.   Andrea Mantegna
Italian, 1431-1506
BATTLE OF THE SEA GODS (left half), ca. 1493
Engraving, 13⅜ x 17¾ in.
The Minneapolis Institute of Arts,
Bequest of Herschel V. Jones, P.68.211

112.   Daniel Hopfer
German, active second quarter of 16th century
Copy of Mantegna's BATTLE OF THE SEA GODS
Etching, 6⅛ x 9 in.
Martin Gordon, New York

The most obvious difference between the original Mantegna (Cat. 111) and Hopfer's copy (Cat. 112) is the difference in size. Mantegna's large engraving relates to the spirit of Renaissance printing, while Hopfer's copy seems more in tune with the German tradition of book illustration. There is also the important difference of medium, engraving versus etching, and certain changed details such as Hopfer's substitution, in the tablet held by the figure of Envy, of his own initials for Mantegna's "INVID" and other indecipherable characters. It is evident from these fundamental changes that Hopfer intended his print as an honest copy.

There is a marked degree of qualitative difference in the handling of anatomy and classical sources in the two works. For example, the face of the Triton or sea-god to the left in Mantegna's print is a quotation from Hellenistic art, an ideal face, mouth opened in an ecstatic expression, hair rhythmically arranged in a "wind-blown" fashion. Hopfer's copy becomes grotesque with nothing in it of classical idealism. Note, too, the lack of understanding of classical proportions in Hopfer's handling of Neptune's back (the standing figure with trident).

114

113

116

113. Albrecht Dürer
German, 1471-1528
KNIGHT, DEATH AND THE DEVIL, 1513
Engraving, 9 11/16 x 7 7/16 in.
The Minneapolis Institute of Arts,
Bequest of Herschel V. Jones, P.68.149

114. Johann Wiricx
Flemish, 1549-1615
KNIGHT, DEATH AND THE DEVIL, 1564 (?)
Engraved copy in original direction
Martin Gordon, New York

115. Johann Wiricx
Flemish, 1549-1615
KNIGHT, DEATH AND THE DEVIL, 1564
Engraved copy in reverse
The Minneapolis Institute of Arts

116. Johann Wiricx
Flemish, 1549-1615
KNIGHT, DEATH AND THE DEVIL, 1564
Engraved copy in reverse with pen additions
Anonymous Loan

Dürer's KNIGHT, DEATH AND THE DEVIL (Cat. 113) is a marvel of invention as well as technical intricacy. Johann Wiricx copied it (Cat. 114) at age 15 to demonstrate his own technical mastery of the art of engraving. To get a copy of a print running in the same direction as the original, it is necessary to make two copies, as the process of printing from a plate reverses the design. The first copy yields a reverse direction print, and a copy of that returns to the original direction. Wiricx did both. The copy in reverse (Cat. 115) is highly accurate and deceptive without the original for comparison. On one of the copies shown here (Cat. 116), a still later hand has added Dürer's monogram in ink. The copy in the original direction is deceptive but fails to capture the full spirit of Dürer's invention. The Knight has a downward glance depriving him of some of his steadfastness, and the devil lacks some of his own power.

117. Albrecht Dürer
German, 1471-1528
ST. JEROME IN HIS STUDY, 1514
Engraving, 9⅝ x 7⅛ in.
The Minneapolis Institute of Arts,
Bequest of Herschel V. Jones, P.68.145

118. Imitator of Dürer
ST. JEROME
Engraving, 9½ x 7¼ in.
Anonymous Loan

This comparison is as highly deceptive as anything one is likely to find. The two prints are all but indistinguishable from each other. The great catalogue of Dürer's works by Adam Bartsch points out, however, that the little toe nail on the left paw of the lion was shaded in the copy (Cat. 118) while the original nail was totally white. The measurements are slightly different too, the original being taller, but this is not readily distinguishable by the naked eye.

119.   Marcantonio Raimondi
Italian, ca. 1480-ca. 1530
CHRIST BEFORE PILATE
Engraving, 5 x 3¾ in.
Martin Gordon, New York

120.   Albrecht Dürer
German, 1471-1528
CHRIST TAKEN BEFORE PILATE
Woodcut, 5¹⁄₁₆ x 3⅞ in.
The Minneapolis Institute of Arts

The Small Passion series of Dürer was done in woodcut and copied by Marcantonio Raimondi in engraving. There is little confusion here, especially as the copy (Cat. 119) omits the signature. Marcantonio, however, has included a small tablet under Christ's feet, and we are told that contemporary print sellers often added the "AD" monogram, as Dürer's name would help sell anything. Dürer was forced to travel to Venice in 1506 to seek assistance in stopping the large traffic in unauthorized copies of his work.

121

123

121. Albrecht Dürer
     German, 1471-1528
     MELANCOLIA I, 1514
     Engraving, 9⅜ x 7⁵⁄₁₆ in.
     The Minneapolis Institute of Arts

122. Photomechanical reproduction of MELANCOLIA I
     20th century
     9.3 x 7.3 in.
     Anonymous Loan

123. Johann Wiricx
     Flemish, 1549-1615
     Copy of MELANCOLIA I, 1602
     Engraving, 9³⁄₁₆ x 7⁵⁄₁₆ in.
     Martin Gordon, New York

Dürer's MELANCOLIA I (Cat. 121) is not only technically one of the masterpieces of engraving, but it is one of the most popular and, therefore, sought-after of all his prints. The copy by Johann Wiricx (Cat. 123), done as an exercise, originally bore a full signature and the date 1602 in the margin and thus is technically not a fake. When, as here, the signature has been cut off, a potential for deception arises. One can distinguish it from the original, however, by the missing symbol between the "Melancolia" and "I" and also by the number "5" in the magic square on the wall; Dürer's is reversed.

The photo-reproduction (Cat. 122) is very deceptive. Framed, under glass, the only possible clue would be in the excessive contrasts of light and dark. Dürer's original has a silvery tonality which does not reproduce. Out of the frame one would find the reproduction to be printed on modern paper and to have a flat, inkless surface.

FORMATVR VNICVS VNA

MELLAN ▪ ▪ ▪ ▪ ▪ ▪ ▪ ▪ ▪ ▪
▪ ▪ ▪ ▪ ▪ ▪ ▪ ▪ ▪ NON ALTER

124

ALL·ILL^AD·ET·ECC^Ma·SIG^MAIL·SIG^R·PRENCIPE
HERCOLE·THEODORO·TRIVVLTIO·etc^ta

MILAN IOYE. CESARE·BONACINA·▪

125

FORMATVR VNICVS VNA

J·R·Meleger Sculp^sit.

126

124. Claude Mellan
French, 1598-1688
THE SUDARIUM OF ST. VERONICA, 1649
Engraving, 16⅞ x 13⅜ in.
The Minneapolis Institute of Arts, The Ladd
Collection, gift of Herschel V. Jones, 1916

125. Cesare Bonacina
Italian, 17th century
THE SUDARIUM OF ST. VERONICA, 1654
Engraving, 14⅜ x 9⅞ in.
Martin Gordon, New York

126. I.R. Metzger (18th century)
THE SUDARIUM OF ST. VERONICA, 1760
Engraving, 15⅛ x 11⅛ in.
Martin Gordon, New York

This series represents a tradition of continued popularity of visual images and ongoing interest in a virtuoso technique. Mellan's original engraving of Christ's image on Veronica's scarf (Cat. 124) established the technical format: the engraved line is a continuous spiral, thickening or thinning out as the tones of the image required. The engraver always worked his plate on a small pad to facilitate turning the plate into the burin. The discipline seen here is a logical extension of this working method.

Bonacina's copy (Cat. 125), done in the same century as the original, is a reversed image, and the engraver has changed the inscription at the bottom; it is in Italian rather than Latin. Further he has eliminated the halo and has "worked up" a bit more the drops of blood on Christ's face.

The 18th-century copy draws on both the original and the copy by Bonacina. While it is still a reverse image and of the same scale as Bonacina's, Metzger has replaced the halo and the inscription that we see on the original. In addition, Metzger has recaptured some of the pathos of Christ's image contained in Mellan's engraving.

127. Rembrandt Harmensz van Rijn
Dutch, 1606-1669
THE THREE TREES, 1643
Etching with drypoint, 8¼ x 11⅛ in.
The Minneapolis Institute of Arts

128. James Bretherton
English, active 1770-1781
Copy of Rembrandt's THE THREE TREES, ca. 1770-90
Etching, 8¼ x 11⅛ in.
The Minneapolis Institute of Arts

This is one of Rembrandt's most celebrated landscapes (Cat. 127), especially as it expresses the tonal qualities of painting in the medium of etching. The Bretherton is an extremely good copy (Cat. 128), differing from the original only in a few instances. For example, in the copy the two lines of clouds in the upper right-hand corner do not reach the shading, whereas in the original the lines run into the shading. Other differences include certain passages where delicate spontaneity in the original is replaced by something a bit awkward in the copy. This kind of qualitative difference can be seen in a comparison of the little men on the right crest of the hill, as well as the horses and carts to their left. Additionally, the surfaces of the two prints are different, the original appearing much richer in texture due to heavy ink left by drypoint burrs, as in the lower left-hand corner foliage.

129. In the style of Israel van MecKenen
A STANDING YOUTH
Ink on paper, 8½ x 5⅜ in.
Mr. James Byam-Shaw, London

130. In the style of Adriaen van Ostade (1610-1684)
DRAWING
Ink on paper, 6⅛ x 7½ in.
Mr. James Byam-Shaw, London

131. In the style of Adam Elsheimer (1578-1610)
GROUP OF FIGURES
Ink on paper, 4¼ x 5⅜ in.
Mr. James Byam-Shaw, London

132. Anonymous
LARGE DUTCH PORTRAIT HEAD
Ink on paper, 14¼ x 10⅛ in.
Mr. James Byam-Shaw, London

133. Anonymous
FIGURE STUDIES IN THE MANNER OF WATTEAU
Pastel, 10¼ x 8¼ in.
Mr. James Byam-Shaw, London

134. In the style of Francesco Guardi (1712-1793)
GRAND CANAL SCENE
Ink on paper, 8 x 12¼ in.
Mr. James Byam-Shaw, London

135. In the style of Francesco Guardi (1712-1793)
GRAND CANAL SCENE
Ink on paper, 8¼ x 12⅛ in.
Mr. James Byam-Shaw, London

139

136. In the style of Francesco Guardi (1712-1793)
GRAND CANAL SCENE
Ink on paper, 18½ x 28⅛ in.
Mr. James Byam-Shaw, London

137. In the style of Francesco Guardi (1712-1793)
ASCENT OF A BALLOON IN VENICE
Ink on paper, 12 x 8¼ in.
Mr. James Byam-Shaw, London

138. In the style of G. B. Tiepolo (1696-1770)
LARGE COMPOSITION
Ink on paper, 18¾ x 13¾ in.
Mr. James Byam-Shaw, London

139. In the style of Domenico Tiepolo (1727-1804)
DRAWING
Ink on paper, 8¾ x 6 in.
Mr. James Byam-Shaw, London

140. After Rembrandt van Rijn
Photomechanical reproduction (calograph)
6⅞ x 6¼ in.
Mr. James Byam-Shaw, London

This group of drawings is lent to the exhibition by one of the most outstanding connoisseurs of this century. Over many years he was a collector and picture dealer and daily dealt with hundreds of drawings. In his years of commerce a number of dubious or downright deceptive drawings were brought to his attention, and he quietly and dutifully removed them from circulation.

They now form a most interesting study collection documenting not only attempts at deception, but also an exercise in discriminating taste. While all here are "fake," they represent varying methods of approach. Some are student works attributed to the master; others are 19th-century caprices done in imitation of and devotion to a style but only became deceptive after the fact. All would test the ingenuity of a potential buyer were they still on the market.

141

142

141. Imitator of Honoré Daumier
MAN BATHING CHILD
Oil on canvas, 13 x 16 5/16 in.
Courtesy of the John G. Johnson Collection, Philadelphia

142. Honoré Daumier
French, 1808-1879
Photograph of THE FIRST BATH
Original: Oil on board, 9 7/8 x 12 3/4 in.
The Detroit Institute of Arts,
Bequest of Robert H. Tannahill, 70.166

This picture (Cat. 141) is an almost exact copy of a documented work now in The Detroit Institute of Arts. The original (Cat. 142), entitled THE FIRST BATH, was painted in the period 1852-1855 and has a fully documented history found in the Daumier **Catalogue Raisonné** which also lists two other fakes derived from this work. While the forger has copied the scene exactly, he has made all the outlines much clearer and more definite than those found in the original. His most glaring failure was the addition of the bold, black strokes on the man and the child which impart a harshness totally foreign to Daumier's style. In the only other noticeable change, the forger has moved Daumier's signature from the lower left to the lower right of the panel.

Reference: K.E. Maison, **Honoré Daumier: Catalogue Raisonné of the Paintings, Watercolours, and Drawings** (London, 1968), Vol. I, ill. I-55, pl. 48 (See note p. 82).

143

144

143. Anonymous
TIGERS DEVOURING A HORSE
Oil on canvas, 19 x 23¾ in.
Courtesy of the John G. Johnson Collection, Philadelphia

144. Eugéne Delacroix
French, 1798-1863
TIGER
Oil on canvas, 60 x 28½ in.
Anonymous Loan

TIGERS DEVOURING A HORSE (Cat. 143) is the type of scene that was often painted by Delacroix during the middle years of the 19th century. This fact and the initials "E.D." are, however, the only things which would link this work to his name. The smooth surface quality of the brush strokes and the insipid melodrama of the scene lack all the intense drama and painterly skill for which the master was so deservedly famous. The style and feeling imparted by this work is, in fact, so different from the true, savage nobility of Delacroix's animal scenes, such as this TIGER (Cat. 144), that it may well be a legitimate work by an artist of considerably less genius to which the initials "E.D." were later added as a means of increasing its market value.

145

14

145. Gustave Courbet
French, 1819-1877
PORTRAIT OF MME ROBIN (LA GRANDMERE), 1862
Oil on canvas, 36 x 28¾ in.
The Minneapolis Institute of Arts, 40.2

146. Imitator of Courbet
HELOISE ABELLARD
Oil on canvas, 25⅜ x 21⅛ in.
The Metropolitan Museum of Art, 29.100.119

This fraudulently signed Courbet (Cat. 146) was acquired by The Metropolitan Museum as part of a private collection, and it was immediately identified as an imitation. The Institute's genuine Courbet portrait (Cat. 145) provides a profound contrast. Where the imitator models very weakly, Courbet presents rich contrasts between light and dark. While the figure in the fake occupies a shallow, unconvincing space, Courbet's grandmother is a three-dimensional volume dominating a palpable environment. The handling of brush and paint, especially in the lace passages, provides a final opportunity to contrast the amateurish imitator with the deftly skilled master.

147

148

147. Imitator of Gustave Courbet (1819-1877)
THE SPRING
Oil on canvas, 19.7 x 23.9 in.
The Art Museum, Princeton University, 55-3251

Courbet problems are extensive and deserving of a complete exhibition of their own. Not only does Courbet's style, especially his late style, lend itself to evocations, but his students' work, notably that of Cherubin Pata, is frequently confused with his own.

This painting, however, is no confusion. In 1969 the canvas was X-rayed and underneath were discovered two additional compositions: one, a portrait, at right angles to the present composition; the other, a landscape with a mill, in the same direction. The style of these two works is not consistent with Courbet's and thus the possibility of the artist's reusing one of his own canvases is ruled out. Further, the forger's style shows a lack of attention to internal detail, yielding a blurred effect which Courbet would not have tolerated. Superficially the work resembles an original, but on closer inspection it fails to hold together as the parts refuse to relate to the whole.

Reference: Harriette C. Hawkins, "Students and Forgers in Nineteenth Century Art," **Problems of Authenticity in Nineteenth and Twentieth Century Art** (Princeton University, 1973).

148. Anonymous, signed "Ed. Manet"
STILL LIFE
Oil on canvas, 20¾ x 25 in.
The Art Museum, Princeton University, 68-538

A splendid example of a fake accomplished with the utmost simplicity, this "Manet" has a rather more impressive background of deception than most. Some ingenious soul, having noted the affinity of style, erased the original signature from this painting and added that of Edouard Manet (French, 1832-1883). This was accomplished at least sixty years ago, as this picture was shown in the landmark Armory Show of 1913 as an original.

The style is really not too closely related to Manet's as we see it today, but more like that of William M. Chase (American, 1849-1916). It has also been suggested that it was Antoine Vollon's (French, 1833-1900) signature which was removed, but this seems improbable.

The painting was lent to the Armory Show by Frank Jewett Mather, Jr. who himself later came to reject the original attribution.

149

150

151

149. Jean-Baptiste-Camille Corot
French, 1796-1875
MISTY MORNING
Oil type on linen, 23 x 35⅞ in.
The Minneapolis Institute of Arts,
Bequest of Mrs. Gertrude Hill Gavin, 61.18

150. In the style of Jean-Baptiste-Camille Corot
LANDSCAPE WITH VILLAGE
Oil on wood, 5⅜ x 9½ in.
Anonymous Loan

151. In the style of Jean-Baptiste-Camille Corot
LANDSCAPE WITH CATTLE
Oil on wood, 5⅜ x 9½ in.
Anonymous Loan

152. In the style of Jean-Baptiste-Camille Corot
LANDSCAPE
Oil on board, 20⅜ x 28⅞ in.
Conservation Center, Institute of Fine Arts, NYU, New York

The late, lyrical manner of Corot has become perhaps the most forged style of painting in the history of art. The landscape format, a low cluster of buildings, a still pond, a prominent breeze-bent tree or two placed to one side of the canvas, and often the inclusion of a figure in a shallow boat, is easily reproduced. As apparent, and assumed to be as easily imitated as this composition, is Corot's flickering brushwork. Closer comparison of the genuine Corot (Cat. 149) with the forgeries (Cat. 150, 151, and 152), however, will reveal the essential difference. Corot's compositions are solidly built up in an almost architectural manner; no matter how ephemeral and transparent the forms appear to be at first glance, ultimately all things in a Corot composition relate as shapes and masses in terms of their edges. The foreground trees in the forgeries simply blend into an indistinct zone, while the village buildings appear pasted to the surfaces. Most telling, however, is the fact that the famous "silvery" quality of Corot's late landscapes results from color and tonality, not simply a few dots of paint dashed across the surface of the canvas.

153

154

153.   In the style of Claude Monet
LANDSCAPE
Oil on canvas, 24$\frac{1}{16}$ x 28$\frac{1}{16}$ in.
Anonymous Loan

This painting is in imitation of a series of landscapes which Monet produced entitled, "Matinées sur la Seine." The series is marked by the subtle reflections of trees and sky in the river, the whole being structured by a highly developed system of color and tone. Unlike the authentic paintings which have a great sense of depth and atmosphere, this work is quite two-dimensional with no feeling of the smooth recession into space so typical of Monet in this period.

154.   In the style of Vincent van Gogh
SELF-PORTRAIT WITH A PIPE
Oil on canvas, 17 x 13 in.
Anonymous Loan

This self-portrait is listed in J.-B. de la Faille's **Les Faux van Gogh** as one of the many fakes offered for sale by the dealer Otto Wacker in Berlin. De la Faille notes that the forger based this work on two authentic self-portraits in French private collections, and, because one had never been shown publicly and the other only once, the forger must have copied them from a monochrome photographic reproduction. This is further proved by the fact that, in the originals, van Gogh's coat is green and his hat blue. The same articles of clothing here are painted with a different and much duller palette.

Reference: J.-B. de la Faille, **Les Faux van Gogh** (Paris, 1930), Cat. F.527 bis, p. 11.

155

156

155. Imitator of George Caleb Bingham
PITCHING QUOITS
Oil on canvas, 40³⁄₁₆ x 58³⁄₈ in.
The St. Louis Art Museum, 159:46

Although signed with his name and dated 1852, there is little doubt that the great chronicler of the American scene George Caleb Bingham never knew this canvas. E.M. Bloch in his catalogue on the artist states that when this painting was first known on the market, it had neither signature nor date and was attributed to Paul Weber, a minor painter of small reputation. The style of this work is more that of the "Ashcan School" of the early 20th century than that of the Mississippi Valley.

156. John F. Peto
American, 1854-1907
STILL LIFE WITH BOOKS, PIPE, AND MATCHSTICKS
Oil on board, 6 x 9 in.
Noah Goldowsky, New York

John F. Peto was a talented still-life painter whose life paralleled that of William Harnett. The two artists knew each other slightly, but the resemblance ends there. Harnett led a successful life while Peto starved. Harnett's works are generally filled with life and vigor, while Peto's are more reserved and mechanical. Nonetheless, many of Peto's "lesser" works have acquired Harnett signatures, as is the case here, as Harnett's paintings on the average bring double or more the money.

158

159

157. In the style of George Inness (1825-1894)
LANDSCAPE
Oil on canvas, 13¾ x 20¼ in.
Anonymous Loan

George Inness was of the generation of the Hudson River School, America's first native school of landscape painting. While his contemporaries emphasized naturalistic details, however, Inness sought a metaphysical union between man and nature and attempted to express this wholeness in his landscapes. Although a certain degree of impressionism is a characteristic of Inness' work, this forgery (a signature appears in the lower left corner) fails to evoke a transcendental dialogue between the viewer and the scene represented. The imitator simply lacked the skill to move the viewer from the heavily worked foreground into the breadth of the middle distance and beyond it into the infinite.

158. Ralph A. Blakelock
American, 1847-1919
THE VISTA
Oil on canvas, 16 x 24 in.
The Minneapolis Institute of Arts, Gift of Mrs. Lyndon M. King from the Estate of Mrs. John Washburn, 47.24

159. Imitator of Blakelock
LANDSCAPE
Oil on canvas, 12⅛ x 14¼ in.
The Detroit Institute of Art, 67.271

Like Albert Ryder, Ralph Blakelock is often imitated, and authenticity is very difficult to determine. Recently an intensive study was undertaken at Lincoln, Nebraska wherein attempts were made by means of scientific investigations to determine the originality of every known work attributed to the artist. Some paintings still defy definitive evidence one way or the other.

Blakelock was fascinated with the effects of light rendered by pigments on canvas and thus experimented widely. In this comparison the faker (Cat. 159) has attempted to recreate the artist's mystical and exotic inventions, where trees surround and overlap a clearing or glade, but has managed only to produce a rather pasty, unconvincing, and flatly two-dimensional imitation.

160

161

160. Imitator of Albert Ryder
MOONLIT LANDSCAPE
Oil on wood, 11 x 10⅜ in.
Yale University Art Gallery, Gift of Robert G. McIntyre, 1950.55

161. Imitator of Albert Ryder
SAILBOAT AT NIGHT
Oil on wood, 9 x 12⅛ in.
The Brooklyn Museum, Gift of Mr. Louis James
to the Conservation Department

In his lifetime Albert Pinkham Ryder painted few more than 150 pictures, but today, thanks to his popularity, there are at least 750. This phenomenon exists for other artists, Corot being the most well known, and to make the point we show here two forgeries and no original.

The styles are different, but both strive for the romantic, mystic murkiness which Ryder achieved by painting and repainting his canvases. So complex are Ryder problems that showing an original here would hardly solve them. Suffice it to say that Ryder saw neither of these, nor the money that was paid for them.

162

163

162. Frederic Remington
American, 1861-1909
THE GRASS FIRE, 1908
Oil on canvas, 27⅛ x 40⅛ in.
Amon Carter Museum, Fort Worth, Texas, 228.61

163. Manner of Frederic Remington
THE GRASS FIRE
Oil on canvas, 18 x 28 in.
The Museum of Fine Arts, Houston,
Hogg Brothers Collection, 43.47

The signature on the original (Cat. 162) is in some ways less convincing than that on the copy (Cat. 163), but stylistically there can be little hesitation as to which is which. The monochromatic paintings of Remington have an internal integrity, and the figures grow out of their environment; they are not painted on top of it. The copy lacks the vigor and spontaneity of the original; where the original conveys a sense of mystery and power, the copy is only flat and contrived.

164

1

164. William Merritt Chase
American, 1849-1916
YOUNG WOMAN IN YELLOW GOWN
Pastel, 20⅛ x 16 in.
Schweitzer Gallery, New York

165. In the manner of William Merritt Chase
TWO LADIES IN A LANDSCAPE, 1960-65
Pastel, 11 x 14½ in.
Hirschl and Adler Galleries, New York

Although William Merritt Chase was noted for his sweeping brush-work and flickery pastel technique, it is apparent in the faked "Chase" (Cat. 165) that most of the looseness is simply an attempt to cover up lack of unity. The figures relate only in a most tentative way to their landscape setting so the transition between figures and grass is "fudged" with rubbing, meaningless dashes of chalk, and dots of color.

The WOMAN IN YELLOW GOWN (Cat. 164), drawn in a much stronger manner, emerges from a deep tangible space. The landscape in the forgery is akin to a theatrical backdrop, flat and unconvincing especially as it fades off the right side of the paper. There is a forged signature in the lower right-hand corner of this pastel, a clear indication that it was created with the intention to deceive.

166. Anonymous
German, late 19th century
STANDING YOUTH WITH CORNUCOPIA
Bronze, 10 in. h.
Shepherd Gallery, Associates, New York

The addition of a famous signature to a mediocre object is a forgery technique applicable to sculpture as well as two-dimensional works of art. In this case the name "Dalou" was incised on the base. Jules Dalou, a 19th-century French sculptor working in a realist manner, had a major reputation and academic approval. Therefore, the forging of his signature on this otherwise undistinguished piece added greatly to its potential market value.

168

167

169

167. Frederic Remington
American, 1861-1909
THE BRONCO BUSTER, 1895
Bronze, 23½ in. h. (Cast no. 32, Henry-Bonnard Bronze Co.)
Signed: Frederic Remington
Amon Carter Museum, Fort Worth, Texas, 2.61

168. Frederic Remington
American, 1861-1909
THE BRONCO BUSTER, after 1898
Bronze, 23¼ in. h. (Cast no. 40, Roman Bronze Works)
Signed: Copyrighted/Frederic Remington
Inscribed to Enrico Caruso
Amon Carter Museum, Fort Worth, Texas, 3.61

169. Frederic Remington
American, 1861-1909
THE BRONCO BUSTER, after 1909
Bronze, 22¼ in. h. (no cast number, Roman Bronze Works)
Signed: Copyright by/Frederic Remington
Amon Carter Museum, Fort Worth, Texas, 6.61

The problems surrounding cast sculptures are subject for an exhibition in and of themselves. Degas and Daumier never saw their works in bronze, as the clay or wax models they themselves made were all cast posthumously. Renaissance bronzes are a deep and thorny problem as to authenticity and have occupied scholars entire lifetimes; the matter has been completely avoided here.

These three casts of Remington's famous **Bronco Buster** serve to indicate at least one problem: when does an original cease to be an original? Further, is one original less attractive and, thereby, less valuable than another?

Number 167 is from the first casting of Remington's first sculpture and dates from 1895. The Henry-Bonnard Bronze Company in New York was the foundry, and the statue is a sand cast with a fired finish. This cast, numbered 32, is distinguished by the loose stirrup, the tail cast free of the body, the smooth leather chaps, and the ears of the horse flat to the body. There is evidence of the artist's making some embellishments to the cast in the finishing process.

We do not know exactly how many casts were made by Bonnard in the years after 1895, but we do know that the foundry burned to the ground in 1898 and no further casts were made there. Those that were have the distinction of being the earliest in a long line of followers.

Catalogue 168 was made at the Roman Bronze Works, also in New York, where Remington moved his casting after the Bonnard fire. It was here that the most famous, most rare, and most individualized Bronco Busters were made, those with the "wooly" chaps. This is made from the lost wax process which allowed the artist great latitude for reworking before and chasing after casting. This cast, numbered 40, must have merited special attention from Remington as it is an inscribed presentation cast for Enrico Caruso. With its flying stirrup, its wooly chaps and, generally, carefully detailed surface this, though later than Cat. 167, is, if anything, more original. Such casts were made under Remington's supervision until his death in 1909.

They did not stop there, however, for the artist's widow had the right to continue casting and, as the molds existed, cast she did. Around cast #80 the tail of the horse was blended into the body; after about cast #200 the model was damaged by an accident and the ears had to be reworked and thereafter took on a rather mule-like appearance. Thus Catalogue 169, while made from Remington's mold, is farthest removed from the artist himself and thus the least "original." Presumably made sometime between 1909 and 1919 this cast is not numbered and could be as late as 1922 for, while Mrs. Remington's will decreed that the models be destroyed after her death, it is known that this was not done for some time. Note that this cast lacks the subtlety and flair of the others and properly comes close to being a mere "reproduction."

170. Alberto Giacometti
Swiss, 1901-1966
ANNETTE
Bronze, 24 in. h.
The Kasser Foundation, Montclair, New Jersey

171. Imitator of Giacometti
ANNETTE
Bronze, sur moulage, 17 in. h.
Anonymous Loan

The original model of Giacometti's cast was made of wax, and the bronzes were made from it in limited editions, authorized and worked on by Giacometti himself. Fraudulent casts taken from finished casts are called "sur moulages" and can be very deceptive.

Shown here in comparison with an original Giacometti (Cat. 170) is a sur moulage taken from another portrait bust of the same series (Cat. 171). Note the dullness and lifelessness of the surface of the copy compared with the vibrancy of the original.

170   171

172

173

172. Imitator of Oldenburg
BAKED POTATO
Painted casting material, 4½ x 7 x 10⅝ in. (with plate)
Mr. and Mrs. Miles Q. Fiterman, Minneapolis

173. Claes Oldenburg
American, 1929-
BAKED POTATO, 1966
Painted cast aluminum, 4½ x 7¼ x 10½ in. (with plate)
Mr. and Mrs. David Ryan, New York

Oldenburg's BAKED POTATO (Cat. 173) was issued in 1966 as part of "Seven Objects in a Box," a multiple published by Tanglewood Press. Originally there were 75 numbered potatoes (1-75), 25 lettered ones (A-Y), and two artist's proofs. Now there are more.

The "Faked Potato" was cast from molds bearing an uncanny resemblance to those used by Dave Basanow, director of the first authorized casting. The fake (Cat. 172) differs, however, from the original in several important ways. First it is physically heavier and more crudely cast. Its chives are only spatters, not globular drops; its skin is dull and lacks the painted-on highlights. The plate is different too, coming from a different manufacturer. But most obviously it is cleaner, being newer.

Reference: Judith Goldman, "The Case of the Baked Potato," **The Print Collectors News Letter,** III, 2, 1972.

174. Käthe Kollwitz
German, 1867-1945
BERATUNG, 1898
Lithograph, 10¹³⁄₁₆ x 6⅝ in.
The Minneapolis Institute of Arts, The Ladd
Collection, Gift of Herschel V. Jones, 1916

175. BERATUNG with forged signature
Photo reproduction, 10¾ x 6½ in.
Martin Gordon, New York

176. BERATUNG without signature
Photo reproduction, 10¾ x 6½ in.
Martin Gordon, New York

The circumstances under which this lithograph (Cat. 174) was photo-mechanically reproduced are unknown. It seems certain, however, that the artist was not involved, for she would likely have objected to the quality of the copies. In both cases the prints (Cat. 175 and 176) are so murky that it is nearly impossible to distinguish two of the four figures. Further nuances are lost, such as the delicate scratches across the upper area and the warmth of the original brown ink.

In both copies the image alone is reproduced on large paper, thereby eliminating the grey "border" created by the original, smaller sheet of paper. One of the copies has a forged signature only nominally like Kollwitz's. The name appears much larger, thereby dominating the bottom edge of the print; furthermore, the forger forgot to cross the "t" and omitted the umlaut over the "a" in "Käthe." He must not have been at all familiar with the German language.

177. Georges Braque
French, 1882-1963
TWO BIRDS, ca. 1958-1960
Reproduction by mechanical process
of a gouache drawing, 4 x 8¼ in.
Martin Gordon, New York

This mechanically reproduced copy of a drawing in gouache was produced with the approval of the artist in response to a market demand. The artist himself signed and numbered the edition of a total of 275 prints. The even quality of the ink on the surface of the paper and the clarity of the edges suggest careful supervision by the artist. Many contemporary artists have sanctioned modern reproduction and printing methods in this way, and many have designed specifically for mechanical printing processes. In this kind of copy we are confronted with important questions about the validity of the unique, or at least limited, object in an age of mass communication and geometrically multiplying data.

178

180

179

178. Imitator of Pablo Picasso (1881-1973)
LE BAIN
Etching, 5 x 6 in.
The Art Museum, Princeton University, 35-1614

Although signed and dated, April 23, 1921, Picasso never saw this print until after it was in circulation as a fake. Reminiscent of Picasso's style of the early 1920s, most of the elements from which this invention was drawn, however, come from after 1921. Signatures, for example, etched directly onto the plate do not occur until 1927, and the woman with her arms folded is taken from drawings of 1923.

179. Pablo Picasso
Spanish, 1881-1973
THE FRUGAL REPAST, 1904
Etching, 18 x 14⅞ in.
The Minneapolis Institute of Arts

180. Imitator of Picasso
THE FRUGAL REPAST
Mechanical reproduction (colotype), 18¼ x 14½ in.
Martin Gordon, New York

Picasso's FRUGAL REPAST is not only one of the monuments in the artist's oeuvre, but also in the development of 20th-century art. It is extremely rare and much sought after.

Shown here in comparison with an original (Cat. 179) is a deceptive colotype reproduction made via a process which does not require that the image be broken down into a series of dots as does a half-tone reproduction. This makes a colotype much harder to detect even though under magnification its lines are characteristically different from etched lines.

Another telltale difference is that the original was printed from a zinc plate and the edges of that plate have embossed the paper. The reproduction lacks such a "plate mark." Inexplicably, also, the reproduction has more shading on the wine bottle than does the original. Since the process is photographically oriented, this can only have been consciously added after the plate was taken from the original with the intention of distinguishing it from Picasso's plate or creating an unknown "state."

181. Reginald Marsh
American, 1898-1954
THE BURLESQUE SHOW, 1930
Etching, 11¾ x 9⅝ in.
Martin Gordon, New York

Because print media by their very nature imply multiple impressions of a single image, the number of impressions is limited, both to control the quality of each image and to maintain the aura of uniqueness traditionally associated with works of art. Historically, a plate or stone is "cancelled" when the edition is completed by gouging or drawing a large "X" across the entire surface. The etched plate in this case was not cancelled in such a way. Rather it was acquired by the Whitney Museum and reprinted. The museum stamped the "restrike" print with its drymark ("WM" in the lower right corner) and sold it as a reprint. Later, someone forged the signature of Reginald Marsh and added the edition number 2/100, falsely indicating that it was the second in an edition of one hundred. This is another example of a forgery resulting from the simple addition of a false signature.

182. In the style of Henri Matisse
WOMAN'S HEAD
Lithograph, 16 x 12 in.
Anonymous Loan

183. POSTER FOR GALERIE MAEGHT
with forged signature
Lithograph, cut down to 20⁵⁄₁₆ x 15⅞ in.
Martin Gordon, New York

184. Alberto Giacometti
Swiss, 1901-1966
POSTER FOR GALERIE MAEGHT
Lithograph, 24¾ x 18½ in.
Martin Gordon, New York

The fact that contemporary artists have enthusiastically exploited mechanical print processes, especially in the field of posters and mass communications, has created a number of possibilities for fraud. Some artists sign their names on the plates or stones; they are, therefore, printed in every image. Oftentimes the signature appears very immediate, as though it were in fact applied individually to each print. Here, however, Giacometti did not sign his poster edition at all (Cat. 184), but a forger added his signature to a "doctored" print (Cat. 183). The printed inscriptions, both top and bottom, have simply been cut off. Traces of the letters are still visible along the bottom edge. This tampering with the original format results in a figure that is close to life-like proportions, very unlike Giacometti's extremely elongated original. A further discrepancy occurs between the shakiness of the signature and the rapid, confident strokes seen in the drawing of the Giacometti figure.

185

186

185.   Honore Daumier
          French, 1808-1879
          FATHERLY DISCIPLINE
          Pen and brush over black chalk, 9⅞ x 7⅝ in.
          The Art Institute of Chicago, The Arthur Heun Fund, 52-1108

186.   Imitator of Daumier
          FATHERLY DISCIPLINE
          Pencil and brush, 9⅞ x 7⅞ in.
          Anonymous Loan

The brilliance of Daumier's technical excellence in the medium of drawing here completely overshadows what, alone in a junk shop, might otherwise be a more deceptive copy (Cat. 186). The intention to deceive is clear in the fact that the signature is moved from the open left side of the original (Cat. 185) to the shadowed right side of the forgery, there to be "discovered." Presumably this was to be passed off as a first sketch towards the later, more finished version. Fortunately the forger lacked the talent to pull it off. Daumier's quickness and sureness with the pen, not to mention his unfailing humor, makes the copy look even stiffer and more vapid than it would alone.

187. In the style of Honoré Daumier
LAWYER AND CLIENT
Pen and ink wash
Anonymous Loan

Daumier satirized many groups (art lovers, the bourgeoisie, hobbyists), but none as mercilessly as lawyers whom he saw fattening themselves at the expense of the poor. This scene of the dispensation of mock solicitude is typical of Daumier's biting humor but is drawn from the artist's vocabulary rather than being drawn by the artist. Curiously these libelous views of the trade are great favorites of collectors in the legal profession today and bring enormous prices when original and enormous lawsuits when fake, as here.

188. In the style of Jean Francois Millet
MAN WITH A HOE
Charcoal on paper, 8 x 10 in. (sight)
Anonymous Loan

189. Jean Francois Millet
French, 1814-1875
HAYMAKER AND A STUDY OF A HEAD
Black chalk on paper, $7^{13}/_{16}$ x $4^{5}/_{8}$ in.
The Minneapolis Institute of Arts, Gift of Mrs. Horace Ropes
in memory of her father, John DeLaittre, 24.45

As a leading member of the Barbizon School, Millet took great pleasure in depicting the landscape and people of the French countryside. His drawing style, as seen in HAYMAKER AND A STUDY OF A HEAD (Cat. 189) is solid and sure, marked by a reliance on a solid outline to define the figure. In contrast, the fake Millet (Cat. 188) is built up with a series of short, broad lines which tend to break the solid outline of the figure. The figural type and shading technique are close to Millet's woodcut **Bêcheur au Travail** and may have taken its inspiration from it.

Reference: Loys Deteil, **Le Peinture-Graveur Illustré** (New York, 1969), Vol. I, no. 31.

190.　Auguste Rodin
　　　French, 1840-1917
　　　NUDE KNEELING
　　　Pencil and wash, 11½ x 9⅝ in.
　　　The Minneapolis Institute of Arts, Gift of Ludwig Charell, 56.27

191.　Auguste Rodin
　　　French, 1840-1917
　　　FIGURE OF A YOUNG GIRL
　　　Pencil and wash, 7½ x 11¾ in.
　　　The Minneapolis Institute of Arts, 23.50.53

192.　In the style of Auguste Rodin
　　　FIGURE OF A RECLINING WOMAN
　　　Pencil and wash, 9 x 10 in.
　　　Anonymous Loan

193.　In the style of Auguste Rodin
　　　FIGURE OF A WOMAN
　　　Pencil and wash, 20½ x 13 in.
　　　The Minneapolis Institute of Arts Study Collection,
　　　Gift of Mrs. H. Gaylord Dillingham

The free, loose style of Rodin's drawings of the female form has long been attractive to the forger. Though deceptively simple, his informal style of drawing has proven to be difficult to reproduce. The forged drawings (Cat. 192 and 193) have not been able to capture the discrete and subtle sense of interior modeling which Rodin achieved with his delicate watercolor washes. As a result these forged drawings remain flatly two-dimensional and evoke none of the quiet sensuality of the originals (Cat. 190 and 191).

194

195

194. In the style of Edgar Degas
BALLET DANCER SEATED
Charcoal and white chalk on grey
paper, 19⅝ x 16¾ in.
Anonymous loan

195. Edgar Degas
French, 1834-1917
YOUNG BALLERINA RESTING, ca. 1880-82
Charcoal on heavy cream paper, 19¹³⁄₁₆ x 11½ in.
The Minneapolis Institute of Arts,
Gift of Julius Boehler, 26.10

Degas' drawings of the ballet are among the most popular of his works. The BALLET DANCER SEATED (Cat. 194) seems to be directly copied from a pastel in the Louvre entitled DANSEUSE SE MASSANT LA CHEVILLE but achieves none of the original's grace and lightness, especially in the dancer's back and skirt. A useful comparison can also be made between the rather clumsy drawing of the legs and feet of this fake and the deceptively simple, essential line used to describe the same elements in the authentic Minneapolis drawing (Cat. 195).

Reference: Lillian Browse, **Degas Dancers** (Boston, 1947), Cat. 70.

196

197

196. Edgar Degas
French, 1834-1917
GENTLEMAN RIDER
Pastel, 12 x 9½ in.
M. R. Schweitzer and David-Jean Schweitzer, New York

197. In the style of Edgar Degas
JOCKEYS
Pastel, 27⅝ x 35 in.
Anonymous Loan

Edgar Degas was a superb draughtsman of the world in motion, and he drew horses, especially as seen at the races, from about 1862. Both of these examples are drawn in the broad manner of the 1880's when Degas exploited the velvety surface of pastels. The GENTLEMEN RIDER (Cat. 196) is seated on a horse of tremendously tense energy, energy conveyed through both contour and modeling. The pair of horses in the center of the forged drawing (Cat. 197) are based on an oil painting dated between 1889 and 1895. Although the shapes are those of Degas, a great deal of the animals' energy is lost in the translation of those contours. Further, as is often the case with forgeries, the forms appear almost completely flat and relate to each other only tentatively.

Reference: Franco Russoli, **L'Opera Completa di Degas** (Milan, 1970), fig. 1165, p. 138.

198

19

198. In the style of Georges Seurat (1859-1891)
STUDY FOR BAIGNADE
Charcoal on paper, 12⅜ x 9½ in.
Anonymous Loan

This drawing is clearly meant as a study for BAIGNADE. It is a close re-working of Seurat's study in charcoal of a seated boy with straw hat now in the Yale University Art Gallery. A central characteristic of Seurat's drawings is his use of tonal rather than linear delineation of form: he avoids the use of isolated dark lines and gives his studies a uniform velvety tone. This example, while preserving the pose and general contours of Seurat's work, lacks his overall pointillist treatment of form and substitutes line and harsh contrasts of light and dark areas for Seurat's subtle blending of figure and ground. This drawing also bears a telltale watermark. Only one original Seurat shows a watermark and that only faintly.

Reference: Robert L. Herbert, **Seurat's Drawing** (New York, 1962), fig. 93.

199. In the style of Georges Seurat
Study for the GRANDE JATTE
Oil on panel, 7⅞ x 5⅝ in. (sight)
Museum of Fine Arts, Boston, 68.75

Seurat's most famous painting, SUNDAY AFTERNOON ON THE GRANDE JATTE, is now in The Art Institute of Chicago. It is known that Seurat spent countless hours making studies for this painting, and many of them survive. Many others, apparently, have also spent time "making" studies for the painting, and the one shown here is fraudulent. This painting, moreover, is more impressionist than pointillist in its approach.

200. In the style of Franz Marc (1880-1916)
BLUE HORSES
Watercolor, 11 x 15 in.
Anonymous Loan

Purporting to be a study for the famous painting in the Walker Art Center, Minneapolis, this sketch is probably nothing more than an admiring copy. While its style has little to do with the graphic style of Franz Marc, the drawing did at least fool one good person once and thus qualifies for this attribution.

201. Emil Nolde
German, 1867-1956
DREAMING FLOWERS, 1955
Watercolor, 12⅝ x 17⅜ in.
Mr. and Mrs. Charles B. Meech

The question of attribution and expertise is perhaps one of the most difficult in all the practice of Art History. Dealers, art historians, and museum curators all are supposed to possess, in greater or lesser degree, the ability to spot both quality and originality. Long and careful study and devotion to one's subject or specialty yields a familiarity with the material which can be duplicated in no other way. It is further assumed that works of art themselves also cannot be duplicated and still hope to pass the expert.

This work is shown here because it has two certificates, both from the same expert, one certifying it as a forgery and the other as a genuine work of art. The first certificate came as the result of personal inspection and the impression that the work in question was not up to the artist's standards and must, therefore, be a fake. This caused justifiable concern on the part of the owners who were then able to document that the watercolor had indeed been originally purchased from the artist himself. Faced with this fact, a certificate of originality was immediately forthcoming.

There is little question that not only is this work original and of admirable quality, but that the problem here is one of beauty being in the eye of the beholder. It is possible that after years of looking at an artist's work one comes to respect certain types more than others, and partiality sometimes overtakes objectivity.

202

203

204

202.   Imitator of Kupka
        COMPOSITION
        Gouache and watercolor, 6¾ x 9 in.
        D. H. H. Turner, Esq., London

203.   Franz Kupka
        Czechoslovakian, 1871-1957
        SPRINGTIME, 1911
        Gouache on paper, 13¾ x 14⅝ in. (sight)
        Anonymous Loan

        Franz Kupka's abstract compositions, while mechanistic, have a
        lyric grace about them both in their color harmony and in their
        geometric forms. The imitator of Kupka (Cat. 202) has managed
        to capture none of the subtle qualities of the artist and only barely
        the general stylistic format.

204.   In the style of Pablo Picasso
        PORTRAIT OF A WOMAN
        Gouache on cardboard, 23½ x 20½ in.
        Mr. and Mrs. Leon Wilburne, Azusa, California

        Upon examination it was discovered that the back of this obvious
        fake bore the stamp of the MGM studios' properties department.
        It apparently had been honestly produced as a temporary prop for
        a motion picture after which it passed into private hands.

205

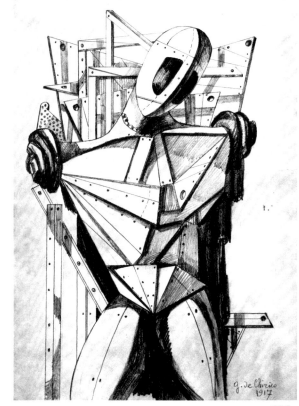

206

205. Giorgio de Chirico
Italian, 1888-
VICTORIOUS LOVE, ca. 1925
Charcoal on paper, 20 x 15½ in. (sight)
The Philadelphia Museum of Art, Arensberg Collection

206. In the style of Giorgio de Chirico
MANNEQUIN
Crayon on paper, 11$\frac{13}{16}$ x 8$\frac{5}{8}$ in.
Anonymous loan

By virtue of his seminal role in the development of the early 20th-century school of Metaphysical Art and his subsequent influence on the Surrealists, Giorgio de Chirico stands as one of the most important artists of our modern period. In 1914 de Chirico began using the enigmatic figures of mannequins as central themes in his drawings and paintings. The strong imposing drawing from Philadelphia (Cat. 205) is a powerful example of this type, the two face-less heads mysteriously engaged in a mute but sensitive relationship.

The forged drawing (Cat. 206) is taken from later examples of the mannequin series produced in the period of 1916-1917, most of which involve two figures. It is unusual to find such a figure drawn against a completely blank background. The authentic drawings and paintings of this kind typically have some sort of architectural perspective to support the mannequin. In its details the shading is also suspect because of its heavy, overly bold quality, a technique which calls too much attention to the geometric elements of the body to the detriment of the overall unity of the composition. As a final note the angular treatment of the barbell-like shoulders is quite different from de Chirico's usual depiction of these forms as rounded discs. This, combined with the rather awkward rendition of the torso, gives ample proof to convince us of the spurious character of this drawing.

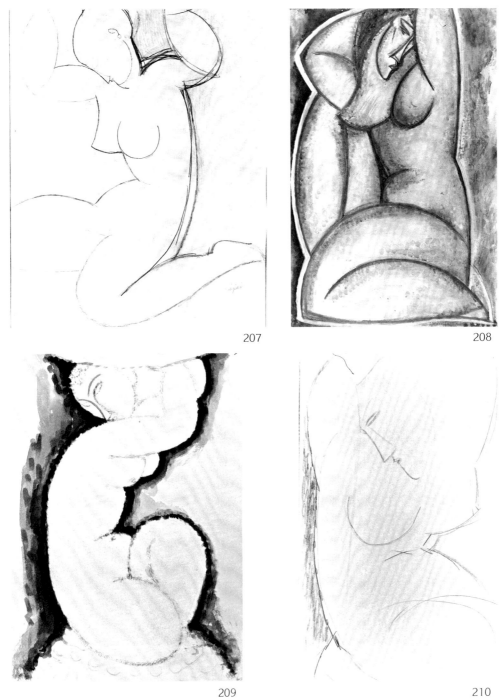

207

208

209

210

207. Amedeo Modigliani
French, 1884-1920
CARYATID, ca. 1913
Pencil and red crayon, 21⅛ x 17 in.
Anonymous Loan

208. In the style of Amedeo Modigliani
CARYATID
Gouache, pen and ink, 29⅜ x 19⅜ in.
Anonymous Loan

209. In the style of Amedeo Modigliani
CARYATID, ca. 1951
Graphite pencil and watercolor, 18.4 x 13 in.
Mr. Joseph Faulkner, Chicago

210. In the style of Amedeo Modigliani
CARYATID, 1915
Graphite pencil, 16.7 x 11.6 in.
The Art Museum, Princeton University, 48-384

About 1913 Modigliani began a series of drawings, watercolors, and gouaches on the caryatid theme. In this authentic drawing (Cat. 207) we can see the artist at his best, combining an essential and graceful curvilinear line with an over-all feeling of solid, stable support which is the very basis of the caryatid figural type. The forgeries (Cat. 208, 209, 210) are in total contrast to the authentic drawing in both style and feeling. Instead of using a graceful system of gently curving lines to describe the female form, the forgers could only manage a cumbersome, overworked rendering which is heavy and dull in comparison. The body no longer works as a unit, but rather each part reads as a separate and unrelated element. The heads are particularly bad in both style and proportion. One should also note the heavy double outline and the meaningless hatchmarks found on the top of the figure of Cat. 208. These are not only wrong but quite out of character in terms of Modigliani's true style.

211. Imitator of Amedeo Modigliani
AMEDEO MODIGLIANI: SELF PORTRAIT, ca. 1951
Graphite pencil, 16¾ x 10¾ in. (sight)
Mr. Joseph Faulkner, Chicago

212. Imitator of Amedeo Modigliani
PORTRAIT OF A WOMAN (JEANNE HEBUTERNE?), ca. 1951
Graphite pencil, 17¼ x 10½ in. (sight)
Mr. Joseph Faulkner, Chicago

213. Henri Matisse
French, 1869-1954
ODALISQUE, 1934
Etching, sheet: 20.2 x 15.7 in.
The Art Museum, Princeton University, 56-50

214. Imitator of Henri Matisse
ODALISQUE, ca. 1959
Pen and black ink, 22.2 x 14.1 in.
Mr. Joseph Faulkner, Chicago

It has been noted that this forgery is directly related to an original Matisse etching entitled **la torse et native nue** which appeared as an illustration for **Poesies de Stephane Mallarme** published in 1933.[1] The original work which is shown here with the forgery is a variation of the 1933 etching. While the forgery is a competent one, it lacks the sure rhythmic grace and continuity of line which lends so much to the balance and proportion of the original. This must stand as an example of a forger's attempt to reproduce a drawing style but failing because Matisse's style is essentially subtle, never simple.

Reference: **Problems of Authenticity in Nineteenth and Twentieth Century Art** (Princeton University, 1973), p. 101.

215.   Henri Matisse
       French, 1869-1954
       WOMAN WITH FOLDED HANDS
       Ink on white paper, 10⅝ x 14⁷⁄₁₆ in.
       The Minneapolis Institute of Arts, 25.32

216.   In the style of Matisse (Elmyr de Hory)
       WOMAN AT TABLE, HANDS AGAINST CHIN
       Ink on white paper, 15 x 19¾ in.
       Anonymous Loan

217.   In the style of Matisse (Elmyr de Hory)
       PORTRAIT OF A GIRL
       Pen and ink on white paper, 20⁵⁄₁₆ x 15¾ in.
       Anonymous Loan

The line in Matisse's pen and ink drawings is sinuous, and the overall quality of his forms, particularly those of facial features, is flexible and organic. In those drawings which combine figures with elements such as ornamental clothing, textile backgrounds, or still-life objects, his tendency is to create definite contrasts between the densely patterned areas and the broad simplicity of figural outline. In this way the decorative effects and the clarity of the figure's line offset and enhance one another. This technique is clearly illustrated in the relationship between the girl's blouse and head in the authentic Matisse drawing (Cat. 215).

   The forgeries (Cat. 216 and 217) fall down in precisely these two areas. The features are a bit too sharp and angular, particularly the mouths and noses, and do not have the rounded flexibility of the Matisse. Secondly, the overall formulation of the composition is too bland, lacking the contrast of dense designs with linear outline. The two pots of flowers in Cat. 216 which should provide the decorative patterns to set off the simplicity of the figure are instead treated similarly to it and thus fail in the purpose of their inclusion.

218

218. Imitator of Henri Matisse (1869-1955)
HEAD OF A WOMAN
Lithographic crayon and pencil, 20.6 x 16.3 in.
Associated American Artists, New York

One very clever fake, sadly not available for this exhibition, is a print over which someone has colored with a pastel crayon to make it appear as if it were a drawing, drawings being worth far more than prints. Here is a peculiarly rare item — a drawing made to look like a print.

   Supposedly number six of an edition of fifty prints, this is, in fact, drawn, not printed, on the paper. The forger has superficially mimicked Matisse's style, but the head does not hold up artistically. Matisse was a practiced and superb draughtsman and would never have constructed a head with eyes which did not match.

219

220

219. Imitator of Modigliani (Elmyr de Hory)
PORTRAIT OF A WOMAN
Charcoal and pencil on paper, 16¾ x 11⅜ in. (sight)
Mr. and Mrs. Patrick E. O'Rourke, Minneapolis

220. Imitator of Modigliani (Elmyr de Hory)
PORTRAIT OF LUNIA CZECHOWSKA, ca. 1951
Graphite pencil, 17¼ x 10 in. (sight)
Mr. Joseph Faulkner, Chicago

When the dealer who sold Cat. 219 discovered that one of his sources, Elmyr de Hory, was a master forger, he hastened to alert all those to whom he had sold works acquired from de Hory of the situation and properly offered them their money back. Most accepted, but the owners in this case declined stating they bought the drawing because they loved it and not because it was a "Modigliani." They still loved it, regardless of the author. Further, they argued, just because the drawing at one time belonged to de Hory it did not necessarily follow that he did the drawing.

With the appearance of Cat. 220, also from de Hory, their case was somewhat strengthened, as it appears to be a copy of Cat. 219. The question now is whether both are copies or versions of still another, original, Modigliani or whether de Hory owned an original which he sold along with a bunch of his own creations to "salt the mine." The judgment here is that both are fakes.

221

222

221. Imitator of Paul Cezanne
Mont Sainte-Victoire (Ex. Coll. Hermann Goering)
Oil on canvas, 21.7 x 18.1 in.
Musee du Louvre, Galerie du Jeu de Paume, MNR528

222. Paul Cezanne
French, 1839-1906
Photograph of MONT SAINTE VICTOIRE, 1886-87
Original: Oil on canvas, 23½ x 28½ in.
The Phillips Collection, Washington, D.C.

Seized by the Nazis during the war, repatriation of this fake painting (Cat. 221) was later impossible as its owners had been killed,
and it thus came into the hands of the State. As John Rewald has
pointed out, it is a conscious forgery of the painting now in the
Phillips Collection, Washington, D.C. (Cat. 222), but it has
a startling flaw. The diagonal in the foreground has been misunder-
stood, as the forger never saw the actual spot from which Cezanne
painted. Rather than a wall it is, in fact, a railroad bed.

Reference: John Rewald, "Modern Fakes of Modern pictures," **Art
News,** Vol. 52 (March, 1953), pp. 16-21.

223. Imitator of Henri Matisse (Elmyr de Hory)
SEATED WOMAN
Oil on canvas, 25 x 19 in. (sight)
Mr. Joseph Faulkner, Chicago

Painted by Elmyr de Hory, this painting is perhaps less successful as a forgery than his drawings, which were his forte, but is deceptive nonetheless. It is reinforced by a "preliminary sketch" which exists for the painting (done, of course, by de Hory too) which attempted to put any potential doubter off the track by simple implication that no forger would have gone to such trouble.

While the colors are very much in the Matisse family, the drawing style is what gives this painting away. Matisse was first and foremost a draughtsman and a creator of linear patterns. Here the drawing is blotchy and incomplete and the more one looks, the more the painting fails to satisfy as a whole.

224

225

224. Pablo Picasso
Spanish, 1881-1973
LA FEMME AU FAUTEUIL
Oil type on linen, 28⅝ x 23½ in.
Anonymous Loan

225. In the style of Picasso
FEMME ASSISE
Oil on canvas, 32¼ x 24⅛ in.
Anonymous Loan

Although in this comparison the forgery (Cat. 225) is not directly based on the original Picasso shown with it, it is very close to the authentic painting in size and subject matter and is from the same period, 1927. Actually copied from an original in the Art Gallery of Ontario, Toronto, this forgery entitled **Femme Assise** lacks any sense of the spontaneous use of line and form which is the basis of many of the master's creations. The thick, precisely drawn black outlines of the forgery become insistently two-dimensional and even take on a geometric quality which lacks the natural grace of the original's sensuously modulated curves.

226

227

226. Imitator of Gris
STILL LIFE
Oil on canvas, 20.2 x 16.2 in.
Conservation Center, Institute of Fine Arts, NYU, New York

227. Juan Gris
Spanish, 1887-1927
STILL LIFE, 1917
Oil on canvas, 28¾ x 36³⁄₁₆ in.
The Minneapolis Institute of Arts, 51.20

While the Cubists used and reused the visual litany which they created, their reprises were new inventions, not pastiches of earlier ideas. Between 1913 and 1917 Gris was developing his personal approach to Cubism. The evocation of Gris (Cat. 226) takes elements from this period and puts them together into a new but not convincing format. The Guitar/Bottle from the Minneapolis picture is one of the elements stolen, but it has been surrounded by the dots of Gris' style some four years earlier. The work is deceptive to the casual eye, however, as its creator has gone to considerable lengths to absorb the master's style and vocabulary.

228. FAIENCE PLATE WITH ARMORIAL BEARINGS
Imitation of an 18th-century Winterthur type
Tin-glazed earthenware, 12½ in. diameter
The Metropolitan Museum of Art,
Gift of R. Thornton Wilson,
in memory of Florence Ellsworth Wilson, 52.60

During the latter part of the 17th century, faience dishes which were modelled after prototypes in pewter gained favor in Switzerland and were extensively produced at the important faience center of Winterthur. The arms on this piece are of the Hegner and, probably, the Egli families who were established in Winterthur during the 17th century. It is entirely modern in manufacture and is believed to have been produced in Switzerland.

229. PALISSY-TYPE PLATE
French, 19th century
Color-glazed earthenware, 16 x 21 in.
Museum of Fine Arts, Boston, Ath 10

The decorative, glazed earthenware produced by the French Huguenot Bernard Palissy (ca. 1510-1589/90) has always been highly esteemed. His most distinctive creation was a large, oval plate ornamented with natural forms found in rural France. These richly colored, ornate plates became very popular in the 19th century, and many potters and factories began to produce facsimiles of them. Bernard Palissy used no mark to identify his work, and, because copies such as this one are almost exact replicas of known originals, their detection usually is made by an examination of the character and type of glaze used.

230. DOCTOR BOLOARDO (figurine from the Commedia dell'arte)
English, 19th-century copy
Soft-paste porcelain, 9⁷⁄₁₆ in. h.
The Metropolitan Museum of Art,
Gift of Irwin Untermyer, 56.30

Commedia dell'arte figurines, an 18th-century porcelain conceit, were based upon stock theatrical characters who performed in the numerous traveling troupes which flourished in France after the death of Louis XIV. Although the lines of these characters were often spontaneous and extemporized, their basic characterizations were well-defined in both role and costume. Doctor Boloardo, one of these easily recognizable characters, was portrayed along with other personages of the acting troupe by numerous porcelain factories such as Nymphenburg, Höchst, Meissen, and Chelsea.

Although a highly convincing forgery, the present example reveals the glaze in a state of decomposition visible to the naked eye. True Chelsea wares, particularly from this period, are rarely seen in such a state.

231. THE MONKEY BAND
Viennese, 19th century
Porcelain, each 5½ in. h.
The Art Institute of Chicago,
Mrs. Alfred Hoyt Granger Estate, 1963.1120-1963.1125

The series of 20 figurines which comprise the Monkey Band were originally produced at the porcelain factory of Meissen in Germany in the mid-18th century. This factory, which had been the first European factory to discover the components which would produce hard-paste procelain, undertook many special commissions at the behest of its aristocratic patrons. The Monkey Band series, intended as a highly sophisticated joke, was ostensibly produced to ridicule the Court Orchestra of Saxony. Although produced in substantial numbers and copied at the Chelsea (England) factory in 1756, these figurines have become quite scarce, particularly in complete sets. During the 19th century, as 18th-century porcelain grew in popularity, these figurines were reproduced at numerous factories, such as the Viennase factory from which the present examples originated. Details of coloring and painting, in addition to the late "beehive" mark on the bottom, however, cast these figurines in a highly suspect light particularly for a seasoned collector.

232

233

232. MILLEFIORI PAPERWEIGHT
Baccarat Glassworks, Alsace-Lorraine
Signed and dated: B 1848
Clear glass and multi-colored glass canes, 3 1/16 in. diameter
The Minneapolis Institute of Arts,
Gift of Mrs. C. M. Skinner
in memory of her mother, Mrs. Harry Whiting, 54.28.4

233. MILLEFIORI PAPERWEIGHT
Modern Italian
Clear glass and multi-colored glass canes, 2 in. diameter
The John Nelson Bergstrom Art Center and Museum,
Neenah, Wisconsin

The Verrerie de Sainte Anne glassworks, founded in 1764 by Monseigneur Montmorency-Laval, became known as the Compagnie des Cristalleries de Baccarat in 1822. During the 19th and 20th centuries this glassworks has been distinguished in its production of paperweights, among which the "millefiori" or "thousand flowers" pattern is probably the best known and highly prized by collectors (Cat. 232).

The modern Italian fake paperweight (Cat. 233), which contains a cane with the date **1852**, reveals its spurious character in comparison to the rich and intricate design of the original, particularly in the lack of depth in the canes of colored glass, the over-all bland tonality of colors, the lack of precision in the forming of the flower-inspired canes, and the numerous air bubbles which flaw the glass. The fact that this paperweight was probably produced to delude a semi-knowledgeable collector of American paperweights is indicated by the date contained in the weight. In 1852 both Sandwich and New England Glass Companies began producing paperweights and, thus, this example, were it original, would be of peculiar rarity.

234   235

234. ENGRAVED TUMBLER, ca. 1922-30
Pairpoint Manufacturing Company, New Bedford, Massachusetts
Glass with engraved designs, 5⅞ in. h.
The Corning Museum of Glass, Corning, New York, 61.4.8

235. STIEGEL-TYPE TUMBLER
Possibly American, probably 1750-1775
Glass with engraved designs, 5.9 in. h.
The Corning Museum of Glass, Corning, New York, 50.4.9

Henry William Stiegel arrived in Philadelphia from Germany in 1750. In the **New York Journal or General Advertiser** for January 14, 1773, Stiegel assured the readers that "the glass he offers to the public, will be found to rival that which is imported and sold at lower prices." Stiegel's success in the manufacturing of usable glass for the home and his innate sense of form and respect for the material has created an aura of desirability about his products which has not gone unnoticed by forgers (Cat. 235).

The Pairpoint Manufacturing Company of New Bedford was noted for its reproductions of not only Stiegel-type wares but also of rare English cottom stem glasses. Highly convincing to the untrained eye, this reproduction (Cat. 234) reveals its true nature only in subtle details of ornamentation, such as the lack of crispness in the molded sides and the somewhat haphazard engraving on the lip of the glass.

236   238   237

236. AMETHYST BOTTLE
American, Stiegel Manufactory, Mannheim,
Pennsylvania, 1764-1773
Blown glass, 4⅞ in. h.
Anonymous loan

237. CITRON BOTTLE
American, Zanesville Manufactory,
Ohio, ca. 1823
Blown glass, 5⅛ in. h.
Anonymous loan

238. CLEAR BOTTLE
American, Larson Manufactory,
New Jersey, 1930s
Blown glass, 5¾ in. h.
Anonymous loan

During the mid-1930s a skillful glass blower in New Jersey began producing reasonably good reproductions of the early Stiegel and Ohio Stiegel-type diamond quilts (Cat. 236 and 237). To the novice these (Cat. 238) could pass as genuine but, when placed alongside the true Stiegels or Zanesville quilts, the differences are quite apparent. Instead of the "flowing" patterning of the early bottles, achieved by inserting the gather of molten glass in a tiny part-size mold to obtain an impression of the pattern and then removing the gather and expanding it to the desired size, the reproductions present a pattern of uniform diamonds which appear to be pressed from a full-size mold. The glass, too, is considerably heavier than the genuine Stiegel, and some of the colors used in the reproductions, the cranberry and reds in particular, never occurred in the Stiegels or Stiegel-types blown in the early glass houses.

As with most forgeries, the cost of mistakes is high. The original Stiegel bottle is worth approximately fifty times more than the fake.

239

240

239. LOWBOY, Chippendale style of ca. 1760-80
Possibly Philadelphia, ca. 1900-1930
Mahogany and pine, H: 29 in., W: 34½ in., Depth: 20⅜ in.
Anonymous loan

240. LOWBOY, Chippendale style
Philadelphia, ca. 1760-80
Mahogany and tulip-wood, H: 28½ in., W: 35½ in., Depth 20½ in.
The Minneapolis Institute of Arts, 15.3

The reproduction lowboy (Cat. 239), simulating the superficial style of the true 18th-century Philadelphia piece (Cat. 240), is clearly not of the period in many details. The table top of the reproduction is fabricated of more than one piece of wood, a highly suspect attribute in a piece of such a date. The exterior wood surfaces also lack the rich patina characteristic of aged wood, an effect which can be simulated but never accurately reproduced. Although the drawers are not visible in this example, an examination would reveal the fact that they are constructed of relatively fresh pine wood, rather than the tulip wood preferred by Philadelphia cabinetmakers of the 18th century. Most obviously incorrect at first glance, however, is the heavily detailed and mechanical carving of features such as the shell-and-foliage motif on the central drawer front which lacks the delicacy, grace, and linear elegance of a true 18th-century piece.

241. SIDE CHAIR, William and Mary style of ca. 1700-1730
American, ca. 1920
Hard and soft maple, H: 45¾ in., W: 17⅝ in.
Anonymous loan

242. ARM CHAIR, William and Mary style of ca. 1700-1730
American, ca. 1720 (with later repairs)
Hard maple, pine and rush, H: 47⅛ in., W: 25 in.
The Minneapolis Institute of Arts,
Bequest of Dr. and Mrs. Vincent Cram, 62.66.1

American "William and Mary style" chairs, the designs for which were based upon late 17th-century English furniture, reflect the recaptured splendour of ornamentation which accompanied the Restoration of Charles II to the English throne in 1660. The American version of this style, somewhat less grandiose than its English predecessor, is evident in these two examples. Although the original chair (Cat. 242) obviously differs from the reproduction (Cat. 241) by virtue of the serpentine arms and the lack of an elaborately carved front stretcher, the general style of the two pieces, as well as of specific details such as the rhythmic scroll-and-foliage crest at the upper back of each, are very similar and highly misleading.

Close comparison of the two examples and a thorough examination of details, however, clearly indicate the two-hundred-year difference in age between them. The reproduction chair reveals only two sets of upholstery nail holes which is certainly suspect in a chair purporting to be 250 years old. All surfaces and carved details of the reproduction piece are also in flawless condition and lack the weathered, mellow look of the original.

243. RITUAL VESSEL, HIEN
Chinese, early Chou period
Bronze, 15 x 9½ in.
The Minneapolis Institute of Arts,
Bequest of Alfred F. Pillsbury, 50.46.90

244. VESSEL, HIEN
Modern forgery
Bronze, 19 x 11
The Minneapolis Institute of Arts Study Collection

The maker of the fake Hien (Cat. 244) has basically copied his vessel shape and the motif of large animal heads from a model similar to the authentic Hien shown here (Cat. 243). In the translation he has made the form of his vessel a bit too tight and severe so that it has none of the elegance of proportion and outline that would characterize a good original. Many liberties have also been taken with the animal decor, not only in its strangely controlled plasticity but also in the juxtaposition of the animal designs for a vessel of this type. Once again the surface condition shows no signs of age or exposure, adding to its condemnation as a modern fake.

245

246

245. RITUAL VESSEL, CHUEH
Chinese, Shang or early Chou period
Bronze, 13¼ in. h.
The Minneapolis Institute of Arts,
Bequest of Alfred F. Pillsbury Collection, 50.46.84

246. VESSEL, CHUEH
Modern forgery
Bronze, 6½ in. h.
The Minneapolis Institute of Arts Study Collection

In this comparison we see a modern forgery of the lowest quality (Cat. 246) juxtaposed with an extremely fine ancient vessel (Cat. 245). The forger has done everything wrong, beginning with the shape of the overly large and wrongly curved lip, the ill-proportioned finials, and ending with the meaningless band of linear decor around the middle of the pot. It seems in this case that no attempt was made to accurately copy an original model.

247. RITUAL VESSEL, KUANG
Chinese, Late Shang period, ca. 1027 B.C.
Bronze, 7 x 9 in.
The Minneapolis Institute of Arts, Bequest of
Alfred F. Pillsbury, 50.46.104

248. VESSEL, KUANG
In the style of the Late Shang
or Early Chou periods
Bronze, 10 x 11¼ in.
The Minneapolis Institute of Arts Study Collection

The most obvious problem with the faked Kuang (Cat. 248) is its unblemished surface, the even dark color being the result of modern chemical patination. In terms of style we can notice its overly tall proportions when it is compared to the authentic Kuang (Cat. 247). This pattern of mistakes is continued in the decoration of the vessel as well. While individual motifs used on this fake may be found on authentic vessels, their placement and combination can not here be justified. A perfect example of this is the animal body which decorates the front of the vessel. It is carried up and actually onto the lid where it neatly joins the large head. This solution negates the usual architectonic character of ritual bronze decor in which the decoration will usually emphasize the individual shape of the vessel and its parts. The more typical solution of extending the body attached to the head back along the lid itself is seen on the real vessel.

Although he may have been familiar with the repertoire of shapes and motifs used during the Shang and Chou times, the forger no longer had the original craftsman's concern for the character of the motif and its formal, interdependent relationship with the vessel as a whole.

249. VESSEL, TING
In the style of the Chou period
Bronze, 13⅝ x 13 in.
Museum of Fine Arts, Boston, F.85

Since the time of their casting the ritual bronzes of ancient China have been revered and treasured, first for their religious and ceremonial value and second as objects of great intrinsic beauty. Although our knowledge of the specific religious uses of these vessels is speculative, from inscriptions and texts we do know that they were used as ceremonial instruments which were involved in a complex structure of ancestor and animal deity worship. The vessels evolved a complex form of decoration which is intricately tied to the symbolic representation of these deities, and, as such, the decoration was highly controlled by tradition and religious custom.

While many forgeries of Chinese bronze ritual vessels are quite convincing, they are usually discovered through a careful analysis of the traditional decor patterns and vessel shapes. The basic shape of this round-bodied Ting is generally correct and follows the traditional types. It is, however, in the intricate decor bands that this faker has made his basic and damning mistakes. The pattern of meanders found on the three bands, although based on authentic models, is completely misrepresented and is not to be found on a genuine vessel. In addition the three animal forms on the lid, the cicada designs on the base, and the animal masks on the legs are wrong in both shape and interior detail.

250. WOMAN WITH A GOOSE, TOMB FIGURINE
Chinese, T'ang Dynasty (618-906 A.D.)
Polychromed earthenware, ca. 14 in. h.
The Minneapolis Institute of Arts, Bequest of
Alfred F. Pillsbury, 50.46.177

251. WOMAN WITH A GOOSE, TOMB FIGURINE
In the style of the T'ang Dynasty
Glazed earthenware, ca. 8¾ in. h.
Museum of Fine Arts, Boston, F.51

T'ang tomb figurines were visual representations of the various aspects of Chinese society associated with the upper classes. The early types were, for the most part, unglazed and painted with colors in the blues and oranges. The forged piece shown here (Cat. 251) not only is finished in the wrong colors, it is also marked by an overly delicate sense of proportion which is out of character with the usual type.

250

251

252

253

252. Ch'en Hung-Shou
Chinese, Ming Dynasty
LANDSCAPE, HANGING SCROLL, 1633
Color on silk, 92.8 x 30.6 in.
The Metropolitan Museum of Art,
Gift of Mr. and Mrs. Earl Morse, 1972.278.1

253. Modern forgery in the style of Pi Hung, 8th century
LANDSCAPE, HANGING SCROLL
Color on silk, 84 x 30½ in.
The Metropolitan Museum of Art,
Gift of Mr. Chang Dai-chien, 1972.163

In this highly interesting comparison the forger has based his work (Cat. 253) on a known 17th-century original (Cat. 252) but has made a few obvious changes. Note the heavy outlines on the lower rock formations and the different form of the mountains in the upper background. The forger has also added false seals and a false inscription which attribute the painting to Pi Hung, an artist who worked in the late 8th century. The forger's reasons for giving his fake an earlier date than that found on the painting he was copying are clever but complicated. In the history of Chinese painting the work of many masters is known only through surviving copies which are sometimes done hundreds of years after the original artist's death. The forger has here set up a case where the 17th-century painting he was copying could be mistaken for a later version of a newly "rediscovered" 8th-century original, or, in fact, the fake he had just created.

254.   Suzuki Harunobu
       Japanese, 1725-1770
       EVENING SNOW ON THE HEATER
       Color woodblock print, early
       impression, 10¾ x 8⅛ in. (sight)
       The Art Institute of Chicago, Clarence Buckingham
       Collection of Japanese Prints

255.   Suzuki Harunobu
       Japanese, 1725-1770
       EVENING SNOW ON THE HEATER
       Color woodblock print, second
       state, 10⅜ x 8⅛ in. (sight)
       The Art Institute of Chicago, Clarence Buckingham
       Collection of Japanese Prints

256.   After Suzuki Harunobu
       Modern reproduction
       EVENING SNOW ON THE HEATER
       10⅜ x 8⅛ in. (sight)
       The Art Institute of Chicago, Clarence Buckingham
       Collection of Japanese Prints

The technique of woodblock printing was not lost in Japan after the deaths of the great Ukiyo-e masters, such as Harunobu. Reproductions made of their prints (Cat. 256) can be highly deceptive.

257. Ando Hiroshige
      Japanese, 1797-1858
      DUCKS IN THE SNOW
      Color woodblock print, 14⅝ x 6½ in. (sight)
      The Art Institute of Chicago, Clarence Buckingham
      Collection of Japanese Prints

258. After Ando Hiroshige
      DUCKS IN THE SNOW
      Woodblock reproduction, 14⅝ x 6⅜ in. (sight)
      The Art Institute of Chicago Study Collection

259. After Toshusai Sharaku
      EBIZO IV AS SADANOSHIN
      Reproduction, 14¾ x 9⅝ in. (sight)
      The Art Institute of Chicago, Clarence
      Buckingham Collection of Japanese Prints

260. Toshusai Sharaku
      Japanese, active 1790-1795, d. 1801
      EBIZO IV AS SADANOSHIN
      Color woodblock print, 14⅝ x 9¼ in. (sight)
      The Art Institute of Chicago, Clarence Buckingham
      Collection of Japanese Prints

These two prints differ both in the cutting of the blocks and the color of the inks. The change in color is most notable in the variation of the blues of the actor's costume at the right, the change in cutting most obvious in the placement of the signature at the left.

While it is likely that both versions were printed within a short time, it is difficult to establish which print antedates the other.

Reference: J. Hillier, **Catalogue of the Japanese Paintings and Prints in the Collection of Mr. and Mrs. Richard P. Gale,** Vol. II (London, 1970), p. 376.

261. PIN
Colombian.
Gold, 2¾ in. h.
The Museum of Primitive Art, New York, 65.61

262. PIN WITH MONKEY
In the style of Colombia
Gold, 4¾ in. h.
The Museum of Primitive Art, New York, 57.129

Colombian goldsmithing displays the crowning achievement of the goldsmith in the Americas. No other cultures, neither the Aztecs nor the Incas, surpassed the care and craft of the very early Colombian cultures. The Sinú, the Tairona, the Quimbaya, the Chibcha or Muisca are all little known. Their exotic names are not so well-recognized as other pre-Columbians, but their achievements are testimony to their rich existence (Cat. 261). They used lost-wax, soldering, and inlay and were even able to achieve heat sufficient to cast platinum. This pin with a monkey (Cat. 262) is a fake which may have been made from a picture, for it is a two-dimensional image of what should be a three-dimensional figure. In addition to this sin the forger used a lead solder, unknown in pre-conquest crafts.

263. SEATED HUNCHBACK, 100 B.C.-100 A.D.
State of Colima, Mexico
Clay, 13⅝ in. h.
The Museum of Primitive Art, New York, 57.8

264. WARRIOR VESSEL
In the style of Colima, Mexico
Clay, 14⅜ in. h.
The Museum of Primitive Art, New York, 57.9

The active and charming mortuary figures of Western Mexico have become more popular with collectors in recent years and consequently more frequently faked. The originals (Cat. 263) come from "shaft tombs," a type of tomb unique to Colima, Nayarit, and Jalisco, Mexico. Here again is the problem of a large body of material from a source which has been repeatedly plundered but not yet scientifically explored.

This warrior vessel (Cat. 264) is all wrong iconographically. Hunchback warriors with slings do not appear in Colima figurines. The patina also appears to have been painted on. It is thought that this piece was probably made around Guadalajara about 1950.

265

266

265. RATTLESNAKE, 1440-1521
Aztec, Valley of Mexico
Stone, 13½ in. h.
The Museum of Primitive Art, New York, 57.2

266. PLUMED SERPENT, QUETZELCOATL
In the Aztec style
Stone, 9 in. h.
The Museum of Primitive Art, New York, 56.292

The Aztecs, the great Mexican kingdom which Cortez conquered, lost a great deal of their art in that conquest. Idols were thrown in canals and all vestiges of the Indian life and religion were blotted out. The Aztec objects which survived are massive, hierarchic, highly ceremonial but rigorously observed in fine detail. It is the lack of careful, accurate knowledge which casts the first suspicion on this plumed serpent (Cat. 266). The real Aztec snake (Cat. 265) is convoluted, but every coil can be followed from head to tail. The fake snake, which represents the great Mexican God, is stacked up in a stiff manner, leading to a head too flat and lacking in modeling. The entire piece is mechanical and dull, displaying nothing of the fine concern for life and death which so characterized Aztec religion.

267

269

268

270

267. STANDING FIGURE, 300 B.C.-100 A.D.
Mezcala, State of Guerrero, Mexico
Serpentine, 3¼ in. h.
The Museum of Primitive Art, New York, 68.75

268. STANDING FIGURE, 300 B.C.-100 A.D.
Mezcala, State of Guerrero, Mexico
Stone, 8⅛ in. h.
The Museum of Primitive Art, New York, 56.306

269. FIGURE
In the style of Mezcala, Guerrero, Mexico
Stone, 2½ in. h.
The Museum of Primitive Art, New York, 59.82

270. FIGURE
In the style of Mezcala, Guerrero, Mexico
Stone, 12⅝ in. h.
The Museum of Primitive Art, New York, 56.326

Guerrero is one of the least known Mesoamerican sub-areas, and currently it is one of the areas producing the most blatant fakes (Cat. 269 and 270). The origin of the real figurines (Cat. 267 and 268) seemed to be centered in the upper Balsas river drainage. Their age is not definitely known. Stylistically they display traits which might be called Olmecoid. These figures are characterized by their frontal straight line, barely indicated features and appendages. They are doubtless easy to reproduce, and again, as with the Teotihuacan masks and Western Mexican material, archeological criteria is lacking because of the fact that almost all known examples have been found in unrecorded and illegal digs. The experts must rely on their sense of style and correctness. Sometimes a microscope may show some trace of a tool unknown in pre-Columbian times. On the other hand, a clever forger will take the time to finish his piece by hand and sometimes even bury it, letting roots and chemical reactions of the soil age and disguise the piece. As Gordon Ekholm said, the skill and imagination of the one who identifies fakes must keep pace with the fakers themselves.

271

271. VESSEL FRAGMENT
In the Aztec style
Clay, 8 x 6 in.
A. Croft-Murray, Esq.

Leopoldo Batres, in a book published in 1909 on Mexican fakes **(Antiguedades Mexicanas Falsificadas)**, states that the manufacture of false antiquities in Mexico goes back to the 17th century. Gordon Ekholm notes that certainly by the middle of the 19th century the fraudulent antiquity was common. Here is an object which was inventoried in a collection in 1861. This crude piece seems to have been made by an ignorant and clumsy workman who put a Toltec headdress on a head whose retroussé nose no Indian would recognize. This object might have masqueraded as the top to a censer of a type unknown by any Mexican culture. What is significant about the piece is its early date.

Reference: Gordon F. Ekholm, ''The Problem of Fakes in Pre-Columbian Art,'' **Curator**, VII, I (1964), pp. 19-32.

272. FEMALE FIGURE WITH POT
State of Jalisco, Mexico
Clay, 27 in. h.
The Minneapolis Institute of Arts, 47.2.30

273. MOTHER WITH CHILD
In the style of Jalisco, Mexico
Plaster, 21 in. h.
The Museum of Primitive Art, New York, 56.144

Both of these figures are "classic" Jalisco types, sometimes called
Ameca Grey, and have as distinctive features tremendously
elongated, occipitally deformed heads decorated with criss-cross
appliqué ornament and large staring eyes rimmed with thick lids.
It was on the eyes that our faker went astray. The eyes on the copy
(Cat. 273) are gouges filled with black paint and have no lids. Other
highly distinctive marks of "classic" Jalisco pieces are the clearly
defined teeth which are visible in the real example but missing in
the fake. The finish on the fake is too obviously "done." Like so
many of the works in this show, the modern pretender got the main
elements of the style correct. It is usually in the secondary features,
in this case the eyelids and the teeth, where the deception becomes
obvious.

274. PENDANT, BIRD
Coclé, Veraguas Style, Canal Zone, Panama
Gold, 1⅞ x 1¾ in.
The Minneapolis Institute of Arts, Gift of Mrs. Arthur Bliss Lane
in memory of her husband, Mr. Arthur Bliss Lane, 63.62.3

275. PENDANT, FELINE-HEADED BIRD
Coclé, in the Veraguas Style, Panama
Gold, 2½ x 2⅞ in.
The Museum of Primitive Art, New York, 58.287

Sometimes it is possible to determine the authenticity of pre-Columbian gold by simply weighing a piece. The old ones are lighter than the new forgeries, the ancient craftsman being more economical with the precious metal than his modern imitators. The fake in this case (Cat. 275) is much too heavy. These artifacts, both true and false, were made with the "lost-wax" process, the flanges stretched by hammering them out. The greater delicacy and mastery of process in the real piece (Cat. 274) would be sufficient to distinguish it; however, there is also a significant stylistic error. A feline head would never appear on a bird body in Coclé iconography. Each god in pre-Columbian times had his own and a few borrowed attributes. Although strange combinations were common, for instance the plumed serpent of Mexico, bird gods in Panama did not sport jaguar heads.

276. BIRDSTONE, ca. 2000 B.C.
Wayne County, Ohio
Stone, 1¾ in. h.
The Museum of Primitive Art, New York, 69.152

277. BIRDSTONE
In the Early Woodland or Late Archaic style, Eastern U.S.A.
Stone, 4⅞ in. h.
The Museum of Primitive Art, New York, 57.77

Although these little birdstone carvings have a wide distribution in the Eastern United States, their function remains unknown. Birdstones have great charm and are easily and, therefore, frequently faked. In these two examples the real stone (Cat. 276) has more wit and grace than the clumsy fake (Cat. 277) with its protruding eyes. Real birdstones also do not tip over on their beaks. It must be noted with birdstones than even the experts are baffled by the skill and ingenuity of the fakers who often do a more convincing job than this example demonstrates.

278. MASK, 300-700 A.D.
Teotihuacan III, Valley of Mexico
Stone, 4⅜ in. h.
The Museum of Primitive Art, New York, 58.250

279. MASK
In the style of Teotihuacan, Valley of Mexico
Stone, 6¾ in. h.
The Museum of Primitive Art, New York, 59.166

The Teotihuacan masks are ideal subjects for faking because of their relative simplicity and because few have been found by archeologists in situ. There is, therefore, no body of indisputable examples to serve as a guide to what is correct. In addition to the lack of delicacy of the carving, which is noticeable in comparison with the original (Cat. 278), there are many reasons to question the fake mask (Cat. 279). In the first place the mask appears to have been dipped in pickling brine. The eye sockets may have been drilled with the same drill that bored the nostrils and the corners of the mouth; a pre-Columbian craftsman would probably have used many different sized objects as drills. The eyebrows, which tend to be slightly more prominent, the appearance of teeth, which is not common in Teotihuacan masks, and the poorly defined nose all combine to cast doubt on this example.

280

280. JAR, ca. 1500
Miztec, State of Oaxaca, Mexico
Marble, 11 in. h.
American Museum of Natural History, 30.3/800

Gordon F. Ekholm of the American Museum of Natural History has described the process of discovering this fake. The piece looked very good although certain surface features and its general appearance served to arouse initial suspicions about it. The execution of the design was extremely good, too good to be the product of some faker's imagination. There was in particular the drawing of the bird in the lower register which could be so perfect only if it had been copied from an original source. A search of the literature revealed that the bird was copied from the murals at Mitla, Oaxaca, which had been widely reproduced. The eagle had been copied in detail as had the two figures on either side. When the jar was compared with the murals, it was observed that the eagle on the jar had no talons, only vague ribbon-like elements, and that the two surrounding figures were missing their lower parts. This was because the murals at Mitla are over doorways and their lower edges have broken away so that there was nothing for the forger to copy. Ekholm remarks that this is one of a few instances in which a fraud has been completely and absolutely exposed through analysis of its design.

Reference: Gordon F. Ekholm, "The Problems of Fakes in Pre-Columbian Art," **Curator,** VII, 1 (1964), pp. 19-32.

281. SEATED MOTHER AND CHILD FIGURE
      In the style of the Bambara Tribe, Mali
      Wood, 28½ in. h.
      Anonymous loan

282. SEATED MOTHER AND CHILD FIGURE
      African, Bambara Tribe, Mali
      Wood, 48⅝ in. h.
      The Museum of Primitive Art, New York, 59.110
      (photograph of object only in exhibition)

Although the overall form of this sculpture (Cat. 281) generally
follows patterns established in known types, there is one important
aspect of this piece which calls it into question. The entire surface
shows definite signs of having been shaped and finished with a
rough metal file, and the strong use of the file is unusual in old,
authentic types. The use of this modern tool, combined with varying
details of style, suggests that this sculpture was made at a fairly
recent date for direct sale rather than for religious purposes.

283. MASK, LO SOCIETY
      Africa, Senufo Tribe, Ivory Coast
      Wood, 12½ in. h.
      The Museum of Primitive Art, New York, 59.295

284. MASK
      In the style of the Senufo Tribe, Ivory Coast
      Copper, 11⅛ in. h.
      The Museum of Primitive Art, New York, 63.45

The use of copper as a material for a Senufo mask of this type
definitely calls the mask (Cat. 284) into question. When this
unorthodox use of material is combined with a strange conglom-
eration of facial features bearing little relationship to known types,
it is enough to identify the mask as a most interesting, though
certainly not authentic, object.

285. RELIQUARY HEAD
In the style of the Fang, Gabon
Wood and metal, 11⅜ in. h.
The Museum of Primitive Art, New York, 56.381

286. RELIQUARY HEAD
African, Fang Tribe, Gabon
Wood and Metal, 13¾ in. h.
The Paul Tishman Collection
(photograph of object only in exhibition)

These figures, called bieri, were carved to be placed on top of bark boxes containing the skulls of family ancestors. Although the general shape of the faked object (Cat. 285) follows traditional patterns, there are two basic mistakes. The top of the head should be much fuller and is too flat on the sides, marking it as being quite different from documented types. The second error is found in the stylized hairdo which adorns all bieri. The faked object shows a hairpiece which has been cut flat by a saw blade, rather than being carved, and made much too short. In original types (Cat. 286) the side pieces would extend slightly below the chin.

287. BOY'S INITIATION MASK (N'TOMO)
African, Bambara Tribe, Mali
Wood, cowrie shells, red kissi seeds, paint, latex patina, 25¼ in. h.
The Museum of Primitive Art, New York, 60.4

288. BOY'S INITIATION MASK (N'TOMO)
In the style of the Bambara Tribe, Mali
Wood, 24¾ in. h.
The Museum of Primitive Art, New York, 59.153

N'Tomo initiation masks are usually carved in a rather general manner without great attention to specific detail. They are found with or without figures attached to the head, but, when figures are shown, they are usually of humans. The most striking failure of the fake mask (Cat. 288) is its lack of the cowrie shells and berries which are human symbols vital to the very sacred and specialized use of the mask in the Bambara culture.

289

290

289. GRADE SOCIETY MASK (BWAME)
African, Lega Tribe, Republic of Zaire
Ivory, 8¾ in. h.
The Museum of Primitive Art, New York, 61.285

290. MASK
In the style of the Lega Tribe, Republic of Zaire
Ivory, 6⅞ in. h.
The Museum of Primitive Art, New York, 57.84

The Lega are well known for their small ivory masks and figures which are very much in demand by collectors. Although the faker used ivory, this mask (Cat. 290) has none of the rich, mellow tone of the original (Cat. 289) which usually comes from exposure and use. Formally, the most obvious difference is in the placement of the facial features. In the fake the features are too well balanced on the typically elongated mask, rather than being concentrated in the lower half of the face as seen in the original. In more specific detail the drilled holes follow no known pattern and are especially muddled on the forehead. Similarly the carving of the eyes, nose, and mouth are crude and not integrated into the mask as a whole, marking the fake as a piece made by someone who had no understanding of the aesthetic background which guided the real Lega sculptor.

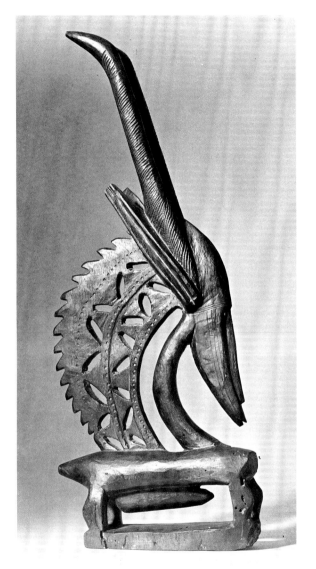

291

292

291. ANTELOPE HEADPIECE, TI WARA
In the style of the Bambara Tribe, Mali
Wood, 27¼ in. h.
The Museum of Primitive Art, New York, 59.315

292. ANTELOPE HEADPIECE, TI WARA
African, Bambara Tribe, Mali
Wood, 50½ in. h.
Anonymous Loan

These headpieces were tied to the top of a costumed dancer's head for use in a ritual dance ceremony. The spurious object (Cat. 291) exhibits many mistakes common to African fakes. The wood employed is lighter and less dense than that which is used in authentic objects of this type (Cat. 292). The carving of the fake is also too generalized and broad, not only in the treatment of the surface planes but in the lack of specific detail in the incised portions. The base and mane are both overly cumbersome, and the entire object shows none of the mellowing signs of human handling and use. The piece was made quickly and insensitively, the carver having no empathy or understanding of the ritual for which it was intended.

293. CEREMONIAL MASK
African
Lega (Warega) Tribe, Republic of Zaire
Bone and feathers, ca. 5 in. h.
Anonymous loan

294. MASK
In the style of the Lega (Warega) Tribe
Bone, 6½ in. h.
Anonymous loan

Authentic Lega masks of this size were carried in front of the face during secret grade ceremonies. As in the case of the forged Lega figure (Cat. 296), the color of the faked mask (Cat. 294) is completely artificial and wrong. Its proportions and overall form seem to have been created for the aesthetics of a Western audience rather than following the seemingly "cruder" model of the authentic type (Cat. 293) which was conceived under an entirely different set of aesthetic criteria.

295. STANDING FIGURE
African
Lega (Warega) Tribe, Republic of Zaire
Ivory, 5½ in. h.
Anonymous loan

296. STANDING FIGURE
In the style of the Lega (Warega) Tribe
Ivory, 5¾ in. h.
Anonymous loan

Ivory figures of this type were only owned by members of a secret tribal society who had reached a specific grade status depending on both economic and ritual endeavors. The color, shape, and drilled detail of the authentic piece are entirely typical (Cat. 295). The forged object (Cat. 296) is the work of a daring native artisan who has created a wholly untypical example, hoping that it would pass as an unfamiliar rarity. The color and head of this fake piece are both entirely wrong although there are precedents for figures of this kind without arms. It remains, however, an interesting example of creative native forgery.

297. GOLI MASK
African, Baule Tribe, Ivory Coast
Wood and paint, 44 in. h.
The Minneapolis Institute of Arts, 62.37

298. GOLI MASK
In the style of the Baule Tribe, Ivory Coast
Wood, paint, 13 in. h.
The Museum of Primitive Art, New York, 59.250

While these two dance masks obviously differ in size, many authentic pieces are of the smaller variety. It is the rendering of the overall form and the individual details which mark this piece (Cat. 298) as a fake, not its size. When used in the dance ceremony, a long grass skirt was attached along the secondary outer edge of the original mask (Cat. 297) to hide the dancer's body. This edge is missing on the fake. In almost all original pieces the horns are quite rounded, and, if there are any incised markings, they run perpendicular to the length of the horn, not along it. Other glaring differences lie in the treatment of the face. In authentic masks the triangles, more often they are pointed ovals, surround the eyes and are not placed below them. The indication of a nose is another uncommon feature. The mouth on the fake mask is ridiculously small and lacks any of the grimacing power of the original. Finally, the overall surface treatment of the fake is much too smooth and general. All of these points, plus the ovoid rather than round shape, mark this example as an obvious fake.

299. FISH HOOK
In the style of the Maori
Ivory, jade, and flax, 5¾ in. h.
The Museum of Primitive Art, New York, 57.100

300. ANCESTOR FIGURE
In the style of the Ramu River, coastal area, Awar (?)
Wood, 14⅝ in. h.
The Museum of Primitive Art, New York, 56.71

301. ANCESTOR FIGURE
New Guinea, Ramu River Valley
Wood and fiber
Musee de l'Homme, Paris
(photograph of object only in exhibition)

Sculptural representations of ancestor figures are common in most tribal cultures where the ancestor is an important link to the spiritual forces which profoundly affect the lives of the tribesmen. While it is often difficult to establish rigid stylistic criteria for these objects, there are certain features which mark this piece (Cat. 300) as being highly questionable. It is, first of all, rather tall for its type since most examples usually are under ten inches in height. The most obvious feature, however, which calls this figure into question is the beak-like nose. In this example the nose is extended below the crotch and is attached to a similar appendage coming from the rear of the sculpture. As the photograph of the genuine figure shows (Cat. 301), this would not be done on an authentic piece. The other most obvious mistake in this piece is the round, full quality given to the body, especially the very smooth and general nature of the carving. The Museum of Primitive Art indicates that the figure may have been made in Europe, possibly in Germany.

302. STONE WITH HUMAN FACE
New Guinea
Karawari River, Southern Sepik area
Stone, 23⅛ in. h.
The Museum of Primitive Art, New York, 62.106

303. STONE WITH HUMAN FACE
In the style of the Karawari River, Southern Sepik area
Stone, 6 in. h.
The Museum of Primitive Art, New York, 67.80

The maker of this fake stone head (Cat. 303) obviously did not understand the basic forms of the style he was copying. By carefully delineating and, therefore, visually separating the head from the rest of the body, he completely changed the character of the type as seen in the original example (Cat. 302). When this is combined with an overly accentuated brow and nose, it gives the face the look of a miniature head from Easter Island rather than of the Sepik area style.

304. LILY PAD PITCHER
New York State, ca. 1835-50
Non-lead bottle glass with applied decoration, 6¾ in. h.
Robert J. and Pamela D. Riesberg, St. Paul, Minnesota

305. LILY PAD PITCHER
American, 20th century
Non-lead bottle glass with applied decoration, 7½ in. h.
Anonymous Loan

Although both of these objects were created by artisans of obvious ability and skill working in identical mediums, it is the mechanical perfection of the object itself which reveals the hand of the forger.

The New York State pitcher (Cat. 304) exhibits a spontaneity of design and execution which illustrates best its own quality of authenticity. This innate sense of freedom becomes obvious when compared with the product of the forger (Cat. 305). The regularity of the neck threading, while skillfully rendered and historically correct, here becomes stiff and uninteresting. The same is true of the shaped handle and crimped base. Combined, these features show us a 20th-century concept of a 19th-century piece.

306. Jacques Callot
French, 1592/3-1635
VIEW OF THE LOUVRE
Engraving
The Minneapolis Institute of Arts

307. After Jacques Callot
VIEW OF THE LOUVRE
Photomechanical reproduction
The Minneapolis Institute of Arts

The original print by Callot (Cat. 306) has been duplicated by a process which can be deceptive since the ink of the mechanically reproduced print (Cat. 307) is raised from the surface as in an original. A casual inspection, however, reveals that the paper of the reproduction is modern and the balance of the inscription is missing.

308. Imitator of Callot
TWO BEGGARS
Engraving
Martin Gordon, New York

309. Jacques Callot
French, 1592/3-1635
BEGGAR **a and b**
Engraving
The Minneapolis Institute of Arts

An anonymous forger has here combined two of Callot's prints into one composition. The style is correct, being copied nearly line for line, but the images have been reversed.

310. In the style of Vincent van Gogh
THE HOSPITAL GARDEN AT ST. REMIS
Oil on canvas, 27⅝ x 35½ in. (sight)
Anonymous Loan

In 1889 Vincent van Gogh painted many canvases of the environs of St. Paul's Hospital in St. Remis where he was a patient. This rather strained and cumbersome copy is a direct forgery of a work of the same title painted in October, 1889. In the forgery van Gogh's usually vivacious and animated brush strokes becomes merely a flat arrangement of arbitrary color patches, lacking any of the vigor and intensity of the original. In detail the line is cumbersome; when viewed as a whole, the painting reads as being flat, dull, and painfully controlled. Van Gogh's directness of expression is completely lost in this self-conscious copy.

Reference: J.-B. de la Faille, **Vincent Van Gogh** (New York, 1939), Cat. 669, p. 461.

BIBLIOGRAPHY

We have tried to gather in one place as many meaningful and diverse books on the subject of Fakes and Forgeries as seemed practical. While by nature incomplete, the listing here is, to our knowledge, more extensive than any other yet published. Many of the specialized volumes have bibliographies of their own which will direct the student of the subject.

BOOKS

Ames, Daniel.   On Forgery. New York, 1900.

Aries, Robert.   Les Faux dans la Peinture et L'Expertise Scientifique. Monaco, 1965.

Arnau, Frank (pseudonym H. Schmidt).   Three Thousand Years of Deception in Art and Antiques. London, 1961.

Ashmole, Bernard.   Forgeries of Ancient Sculpture. Oxford, 1962.

Ballo, Quido.   Vero e Falso nell'Arte Moderna. Turin, 1962.

Barber, A.E.   Ceramic Forgeries. Philadelphia, 1907.

Baroni, Fiorenzia. Osservazioni sul Trono di Boston. Rome, 1961.

Batres, Leopoldo.   Antiquedades Mexicanas Falsificadas. Mexico, 1909.

Bauer and Rinnebach.   L'Examen des Peintures aux Rayons X…Mouseion, 1931.

Beaumont, Alvin.   Autour de Watteau. Paris, 1932.

Beauvais, R.   La Maniere de Distinguer le…Counterfeites. Paris, 1939.

Beissel, Stephan. Gefalschte Kunstwerke. Freiburg, 1909.

Berger, Ernst.   Beitrage Zur Entwicklungsgeschichte der Maltechnick. Munich, 1901.

Blackburn, D. and W. Cadell.   The Detection of Forgery. New York, 1959.

Bonaffe, Edmond.   Causeries sur L'Art et la Curiosite. Paris, 1878.

Borchardt, Ludwig.   Agyptische "Altertumen" Die ich fur Neugezeitlich Halte. Berlin, 1930.

Brunori, Dionisio.   Giovanni Bastianini. Florence, 1906.

Brusse, M.J.   Knoeiorijen in den Schildeijenhandel. Rotterdam, 1926.

Bulley, M.H.   Art and Counterfeit. London, 1926.

Burckhardt, Jacob.   Uber die Echteit Alter Bilder (unpublished thesis). Statsarchiv Basel, 1882.

Burroughs, Alan.   Art Criticism from a Laboratory. Boston, 1938.

Cartault, A.   Sur L'Authenticite des Groupes. Macon, 1887.

Cerdeira, E.   Duas Grandes Fraude e Camonianas. Barcelona, 1946.

Cescinsky, Herbert.   The Gentle Art of Faking Furniture. London, 1913.

Cole, Sonia.   Counterfeit. London, 1955.

Cooney, John.   Assorted Errors in Art Collecting. Philadelphia, 1963.

Coremans, Dr. P.B.   Van Meegeren's Faked Vermeers and de Hooghs. Amsterdam, 1949.

Cramer, Hans.   Die Behandlung der Kunstfalschung im Privatrecht. Zurich, 1947.

Dangers, R.   Die Rembrandt — Falschungen. Hanover, 1928.

Dantzig, M.   Illunstwerk, Maakwerk, Vervalsching. Amsterdam, 1937.

Decoen, J.   Back to the Truth. Rotterdam/London, 1951.

Demeure, Fernand.   Les Impostures de L'Art. Paris, 1951.

Donath, A.   Wie Die Kunstfalscher Arbeiten. Prague, 1937.

Edel, Pablo.   La Falsificacion de Antiquedades y Objectos de Art. Buenos Aires.

Eudel, Paul.   Falscherkunste. Leipzig, 1909.

Eudel, Paul.   Trucs et Truqueurs. Paris, 1907.

Eudel, Paul. Le Truguage les Contrefaçons Devoilees. Paris, 1884.

Eudel, Paul and Arthur Roesslel.   Art Frauds, Forgeries and Fakes. New York, 1948.

Eudel, Paul and Arthur Roesslel.   Falscherkunst. Vienna, 1947.

Ewald, W.   Siegelmissbrauch und Siegelfalschung im Mittelalter..Treves, 1911.

Faille, Jacob de la.   Les Faux van Gogh. Paris/Brussels, 1930.

Farrer, J.A.   Literary Forgeries. London, 1907.

Finzi, M.   La Fotografia Quale Mezzo si Scopertha Deue Falsita in Documenti. Florence, 1911.

Fischer-Bothhof, E.   Echte Falschungen. Berlin, 1947.

Foresi, A.   Tour de Babel ou Objects D'Art Faux Paris Pour Vrai et Vice-Versa. Florence, 1868.

Foresi. M.   Di Un Valoroso Scultore (Giovanni Bastianini). Florence, 1911.

Friedländer, Max.   Echt Und Unecht Aus Erfahrungen Des Kunstkenners. Berlin, 1929.

Friedländer, Max.   Genuine and Counterfeit. New York, 1930.

Friedländer, Max.   On Art and Connoisseurship. London, 1942.

Froentjes, W.   Criminalistic Aspects of Art Forgery (a paper on the Aspects of Art Forgery presented at the Institute of Criminal Law and Criminology, University of Leiden). The Hague, 1962.

Furtwangler, Adolf.   Neure Falschung von Antiken. Berlin, 1899.

Furdaux, R.   Fact, Fake or False? London, 1954.

Gabrol, F. and H. Leclerq.   Dictionaire Diarcheologie Chretienne et du Liturgie, Vol. I-IV. Paris, 1907-1939.

Ganneau, Charles.   Les Fraudes Archeologiques en Palestine. Paris, 1885.

Godley, John.   The Master Forger: the Story of Han van Meegeren. London, 1951.

Goldschmidt, A.   Elfenbeinskulpturen, Vol. I. Berlin, 1914-1924.

Goldschmidt, A. and Kurt Weitzman. Byzantinische Elfenbeinskulpturen, Vol. II. Berlin, 1930-1934.

Goll, Yoachim. Kunstfalscher. Leipzig, 1962.

Grabke, H.A. Die Wandmalereien der Marienkirche Zu Lubeck. Hamburg, 1951.

Hahn, Harry. The Rape of La Belle. Kansas City, 1946.

Hammond, Dorothy. Confusing Collectibles. Des Moines, 1969.

Hannover, Emile. Pottery and Porcelain. London, 1925.

Hayward, Charles H. Antique or Fake? London, 1970.

Hector, L.C. Palaeography and Forgery. New York, 1959.

Heller, David. In Search of V.O.C. Glass. Capetown, 1951.

Hellwig, Hellmuth. Einbandfalschungen. Stuttgart, 1968.

Hessel, A. Von Modernen Falschungen. Munich, 1931.

Hollander, Barnett. The International Law of Art. London, 1959.

Hovo, Paul. L'Art de Distinguer les Faux. Saigon, 1930.

Irving, Clifford. Fake! New York, 1969.

Isnard, Guy. Faux et Imitations dans l'art, Vol. I and II. Paris, 1959-1960.

Ivins, W.M., Jr. How Prints Look. Boston, 1943.

Jepson, Lawrence. The Fabulous Frauds. New York, 1970.

Joni, I.C. The Affairs of a Painter. London, 1936.

Jones, H.M. Facsimilies and Forgeries. Ann Arbor, 1934.

Jouseaume, F. Les Vandales du Louvre. Paris, 1910.

Karl, Robert. Les Imitations Ceramiques. Paris, 1896.

Kilbracken, Baron John. Van Meegeren: A Case History. Bristol, 1967.

Koppen, Walter. Kunst and Kunstfalschungen. Wiefeld, 1912.

Kurtz, Otto. Fakes. New Haven, 1948.

Lang, Andrew. The Clyde Mystery.... 1905.

Laurie, Arthur P. New Light on Old Masters. London, 1914.

Laurie, Arthur P. The Technique of the Great Painters. London, 1949.

Lee, Ruth Webb. Antique Fakes and Reproductions. Framingham Center, 1939.

Linder, Paul. Arte Autentics, Arte Copiado, Arte Restourado, Arte Falsificado. Lima, 1956.

Litchfield, Fredrick. Antiques: Genuine and Spurious. London, 1924.

Livinsky, A. Tosoro Sacro Rossi. Roma, 1964.

Lu, Shih-hua. Scrapbook for Chinese Collectors: A Chinese Treatise on Scrolls and Forgers. Beirut, 1958.

Lusetti, Walter. Alceo Dossena. Rome, 1955.

Madsen, Herman. Kunstforfalsching. Odense, 1945.

Mailfert, Andre. Au Pays des Antiquaires. Paris, 1935.

Mansoor, Edmond R. Je Cherche un Homme. Los Angeles, 1971.

Marschal, A.A. La Ceramique et les Faussaires. Paris, 1875.

Maskell, A. Ivories. London, 1905.

Meder, Josef. Falschungen Von Handzeichnungen.... Vienna, 1921.

Menant, Joachim. Les Fausses Antiquites de L'Assyrie.... Paris, 1888.

Mendax, Fritz. Art Fakes and Forgeries. London, 1955.

Mitchell, C.A. The Expert Witness. Cambridge, 1923.

Mowbray, Andrew E. and Stephen V. Grancsay. Arms and Armor From the Atelier of Ernst Schmidt. Providence, 1967.

Munro, R. Archeology and False Antiquities. London, 1905.

Neuburger, Albert. Echt Oder Falschung? Leipzig, 1924.

Nicolay, Jean. ...L'Art et la Maniere des Maitres Ebenistes. Paris, 1953.

Osborn, Albert S. Questioned Documents. London, 1929.

Ortloff, Hermann. Falschung, Betrug. Jena, 1862.

Paul, Eberhard. Die Falsche Gottin.... Heidelburg, 1962.

Paul, Eberhard. Studien Zu Problematik der Antikerfalschungen. Leipzig, 1963.

Piccard, Gerard. ...Der Magdelenen Altar des "Lukas Moser." Weisbaden, 1969.

Planiscig, L. and A. Weixlgartner. Festschrift Julius Schlosser. Vienna, 1927.

Porkay, Martin. Die Abenteuer Zweier Unechter Rembrandts. Munich, 1963.

Raehlmann, E. Uber die Maltechnik der Alten. Leipzig, 1910.

Rienaecker, Victor. Paintings and Drawings of J.B.C. Corot.... London/New York, 1929.

Riepenhausen, F.G. Peinture de Polygnote a Delphes.... Rome, 1826.

Reisner, Robert G. Fakes and Forgeries in the Fine Arts. New York, 1950.

Rheims, M. The Strange Life of Objects. New York, 1961.

Rieth, Adolf (tr. Diana Imber). Archeological Fakes, London, 1970.

Robinson, F.S. Frauds and Forgeries. New York, 1897.

Rorrimer, J. Ultra Violet Rays and Their Use in Examination of Works of Art. New York, 1931.

Savage, George. Forgeries, Fakes and Reproductions. London, 1963.

Schauss, Martin. Die Leonardische Flora.... Leipzig, 1910.

Schmitt, Heinrich. Arte Della Falsificazione.... Milan, 1960.

Schrade, Hubert. Das Problem des Kunstfalschertums. Stuttgart, 1963.

Schüller, Sepp. Falsch Oder Echt? Bonn, 1953.

Schüller, Sepp. Forgers, Dealers, Experts. New York, 1960.

Seelig, E. Kunstwerkfalschung. Berlin, 1940.

Seelman, Theo. Unechte Kunstwerke. Stuttgart, 1892.

Seling, Helmut. Keysers Kunst — und Antiquitätenbuch, Heidelburg, 1957-59.

Sergant, Philip W. Liars and Fakers. London, 1925.

Sheppard, T. Forgeries and Counterfeit Antiquities. Hull, 1908.

Staring, A. Kunsthistorische Verkenningen. Berlin, 1948.

Stevens, Joseph. Flint Jack. Rendin, 1894.

Symonds, R.W. The Present State of Old English Furniture. London, 1923.

Thausing, M. Zur Falschung Alter Kunstwerke. Leipzig, 1884.

Tietze, Hans. Genuine and False: copies, imitations, forgeries. New York, 1948.

Treve, Wilhelm. Art Plunder. London, 1960.

Turrel, Siegfried (editor). Falschungen. Grazi, 1930.

Valdon, Rene. De la Contrefacon des Oeuvres D'Art Aux Etats-unis. Paris, 1888.

Valentini, P.T. Mayan Forgery. Worchester, 1880.

Valmount, Claude. Antiquaries des Grandes Dremis. Paris, 1930.

Van de Waal, H. Forgery as a Stylistic Problem (a paper on the Aspects of Art Forgery presented at the Institute of Criminal Law and Criminology, University of Leiden). The Hague, 1962.

Vayson de Pradenne, A. ...Les Fraudes in Archeologie Pre-historique. Paris, 1932.

Wakling, T.G. Forged Egyptian Antiquities. London, 1912.

Walker, Rainforth A. How to Detect a Beardsley Forgery. Bedford, 1950.

Wallagh, B. De Echte Van Meegeren. Amsterdam, 1947.

Weiner, J.S. The Piltdown Forgery. Oxford, 1954-55.

Weller, Emil. Die Falschen und Fingierten Druckorte. Leipzig, 1864.

Westwood, J. Fictile Ivories in the South Kensington Museum. London, 1876.

The Whitney Museum. The Problem of Authenticity in American Art. New York, 1942.

Wolters, C. ...Rontgen Straflen fur Die Kunstgeschichte. Frankfort, 1938.

Würtenberger, Thomas. Das Kunstfalschertum. Weimar, 1940.

Würtenberger, Thomas. Der Kampf Gegen das Kunstfal-schertum in der Deutschen und Schweizerischen Strafrechtspfkege. Weisbaden, 1951.

Würtenberger, Thomas. Criminological and Criminal Law Problems of the Forging of Painting (a paper on the Aspects of Art Forgery presented at the Institute of Criminal Law and Criminology, University of Leiden). The Hague, 1962.

Yates, Raymond F. Antique Fakes and Their Detection. New York, 1950.

PERIODICALS

Amyx, D.A. "Forged Corinthian Animal Frieze," Brooklyn Museum Bulletin, II, pp. 9-13. Spring, 1960.

Abas, S. P. "Valsch En Echt," Maanblad Voor Beeldende Kunsten, XII, pp. 18-22. January, 1935.

Atkinson, R.J.C. "The Llanrwst Bracelet," Bulletin of the Board of Celtic Studies, XVIII, pp. 206-207. 1958-1960.

Alevedo, Michelangelo Cagiano De. "Falsi Settecenteschi di Pittura Antiche," Bolletino dell'Instituto Centrale, I, pp. 41-43. 1950.

Bailey, D. M. "False Roman Lamp," Archaeology, XI, p. 126. June, 1958.

Banister, J. "Forgers, Furbishers, and Duty-dodgers," Apollo, LXXV, pp. 104-107. October, 1961.

Barstow, Nina. "The Romance of Art...," Magazine of Art V, 9, pp. 503-508. 1886.

Basler, A. "Falscherkandale," Kunst und Kunstler, XXVIII, pp. 431-432. July, 1930.

Baumgart, F. "Zu Den Dossena Falschungen," Zeitschrift fur Bildende Kunst, LXIII, pp. 1-3. April, 1929.

Bazin, Germain. "Le Problem de l'Authenticite dans L'Oeuvre de Corot," Bulletin du Laboratoire du Musée du Louvre, pp. 30-35. June, 1956.

Beard, C.R. "...A Nineteenth Century Fake Exposed," Connoisseur, CI, pp. 171-175. April, 1938.

Beard, C.R. "Too Good To Be True...," Connoisseur, LXXXIX, pp. 218-225. April, 1932.

Bertheholt, D. and G. B. Guardia. "New Laboratory for the Scientific Investigation of Paintings," Fine Arts, XVIII, p. 58. December, 1931.

Biglow, E. "Fraudulent Inlaid Box," Studio, II, pp. 26-30. July, 1933.

Blom, J. "Falsh Oder Echt...?" Weltkunst, XXII, 20, p. 3. 1952.

Blum, Andre. "...Une Fraude Archeologigue," Congres d'Histoire de L'Art, II, pp. 617-626. 1924.

Blunt, A. "...Early Falsifications of Poussin," Burlington Magazine, CIV, pp. 486-498. November, 1962.

Bolce, Harold. "The Truth About Gothic Fakes," Arts and Decor, XIX, pp. 9-11. September, 1923.

Bopkin, Thomas. "An Unrecorded Botticelli," Burlington Magazine, LXII, p. 362. May, 1933.

Bordley, J. "...Scientific Methods Used in Expertising...," Art Digest, XXIII, p. 6. May, 1949.

Born, W. "Ancient Forgeries of Works of Art," Apollo, XXXII, pp. 5-10. July, 1940.

Boswell, H. "Van Meegeren and his Vermeers," Art Digest, XXII, p. 4. February, 1941.

Bothmer, Dietrich von. "An Inquiry into the Forgery of the Etruscan Terracotta," The Metropolitan Museum of Art Bulletin, 1961.

Bower, Anthony. "The Double Dealers," Art in America, LVI, 4, pp. 58-59. 1968.

Brainerd, George W. "Another Falsified Maya Codex," Masterkey, XXII, pp. 17-18. January, 1948.

Breck, Joseph. "The Ficoroni Medallion," Art Bulletin, IX. June, 1927.

Brevil, H. "Stories About Fakes," Antiquity, XXIX, pp. 196-198. December, 1955.

Bridgman, Margaret. "Gardens That Grow Old Masters," International Study, V, 75, pp. 158-160. 1922.

Brown, W.N. "Fraud in Jewelry and Precious Stones," Connoisseur, V, pp. 198-200. March, 1903.

Buren, A.W. "Forged Antiquities," Parnassus, I, p. 8. April, 1929.

Burroughs, Alan. "X-Raying the Truth about Old Masters," Arts, IX, pp. 325-333. 1926.

Burroughs, Alan. "Bronzino X-Rayed...," Creative Art, VII, pp. 222-224. September, 1930.

Calder, W.M. "Missak, Stone Cutter," Journal of Hellenic Studies, XLVII, pp. 178-179. 1927.

Carrol, D.L. "...Identification of Forgeries in Ancient Jewelry," American Journal of Archaeology, LXXIV, p. 401. October, 1970.

Chambaudet, Jaques. "Les Faux en Peinture," Revue, pp. 351-354. January, 1949.

Chanin, A.L. "Counterfeits and Conservation: Two Exhibitions...," Art Digest, XXVIII, p. 10. February, 1954.

Charles, J. "Les Plus Grands Faux...," France Illustration, CDXXIV, pp. 66-68. July, 1955.

Chastel, Andre. "Le Musee Du Faux," Medecine de France, 52, pp. 42-44. 1954.

Chevelier-Verel, Mme. "Faux en Prehistoire," L'Amour de L'Art. November, 1932.

Chevelier-Verel, Mme. "Prehistoire et Faussaires," L'Amour de L'Art, XIII, pp. 293-296. November, 1938.

Cole, S. "Forgeries and the British Museum," Antiquity, XXXV, pp. 103-106. June, 1961.

Colin, Ralph and Dudley Easby. "The Legal Aspects of Forgery," Metropolitan Museum of Art Bulletin, XXVI, pp. 257-261. 1967-1968.

Colin, Ralph F. "Fakes and Frauds in the Art World," Art in America, LI, pp. 86-89. April, 1963.

Coplan, N. and B. Thomson. "Can an Architect be Charged with Fraud?" Progressive Architecture, XLI, p. 7. January, 1960.

Coremans, P.B. "...The Case of Van Meegeren," Magazine of Art, XLI, pp. 192-193. May, 1948.

Coremans, P.B. "L'Affaire des Faux Vermeer...," Maanblad Voor Beeldene Kunsten, XXVI, pp. 199-203. 1950.

Croft-Murray, E. "An Exhibition of Forgeries...," British Museum Quarterly, XXIV, pp. 29-30. 1961.

Courjod, L. "L'Imitation et la Contrefacon des Objects d'Art Antiques," Gazette des Beaux-Arts. 1887.

Decoen, J. "Le Faux Vermeer...," Arts, I. August, 1946.

Delogu, G. "Vienna: Una Esposizione Di Falsi," Emporium, LXXXVI, pp. 566-567. October, 1937.

Douglas, L. "Photographic Evidence," Burlington Magazine, 60, pp. 280-289. June/July, 1932.

Dunham, D. "Ancient Egyptian Forgery...?" Museum of Fine Arts Bulletin, Boston, XXXI, pp. 79-81. October, 1933.

Durer, A.L. and F. Stephens and T. Whitburn. "Affidavits Concerning the Wax Bust of Flora," Burlington Magazine, XVII, pp. 178-183. April, 1910.

Ekholm, Gordon F. "The Problem of Fakes in Pre Columbian Art," Curator, VII, 1, pp. 19-32. 1964.

Eliot, Wallace. "Reproductions and Fakes of English 18th Century Ceramic," English Ceramic Circle Transaction, 7, pp. 67-82. 1939.

Eliot, William J. "The Use of Roentgen Ray in the Scientific Examination of Painting," American Journal of Roentgenology and Radium Therapy, L, 6. December, 1943.

Elville, E.M. "Early Worchester Reproductions," Country Life, CXI, pp. 88-89. January, 1952.

Erman, Adolf and H. Shäfer. "Der Angebliche Agyptische Bericht Über Die Umschiffung Afrikas," Sitzungbericht D.K.P. Akademie der Wissenschaft. July, 1908.

Faille De La, J.B. "False Van Gogh," Formes, I, p. 10-11. December, 1929.

Faille De La, J.B. "...A Propos of the False Van Gogh," L'Art Vivant, VI, pp. 483-484. June, 1930.

Fell, H.G. "Validity of Fakes as Works of Art," Connoisseur, CXII, pp. 32-37. March, 1946.

Field, H.E. "The False Renoirs...," Arts, I, pp. 18-24. 1920.

Fischel, Oskar. "A Forger of Raphael Drawings," Burlington Magazine, LI, pp. 26-31. 1927.

Fong, W. "A Problem of Forgeries in Chinese Painting," Artibus Asiae, II, pp. 95-140. 1962.

Fong, W. "Chinese Album and its Copy," Princeton Museum Record, XXVII, pp. 74-78. 1968.

Frankenstein, Alfred. "Harnett True and False," Art Bulletin, pp. 46-48. March, 1949.

Frankfurter, Alfred. "The Gentle Art of Faking," Art News, LXI, 10, pp. 16-19. 1954.

Fraser, P.M. "Some Alexandrian Forgeries," Proceedings of the British Academy, XLVII, pp. 243-250. 1961.

Friedländer, M.J. "Artistic Quality: Original and Copy," Burlington Magazine, LXXVIII, pp. 143-148. May, 1941.

Friedländer, M.J. "On Forgeries," Burlington Magazine, LXXVIII, pp. 192-197. June, 1941.

Furst, H. "Value of Forgeries," Apollo, XLII, p. 242. October, 1945.

Gan, P. "Original, Kopie, and Fälschung," Die Umschau. 1949.

Gläser, Curt. "Die Gefälschte Kunst…," Kunst und Kunstler, XXVIII, pp. 291-294. 1924.

Gläser, Curt. "Die Van Gogh Affaire," Kunst und Kunstler, XXVII, pp. 131-136. January/February, 1929.

Goldman, Judith. "The Case of the Baked Potato," Print Collectors News Letter, III, 2. May, 1973.

Goldschmidt, A. Sitzungsberichte Preuss Akademie der Wissenschaft, pp. 586-587. July, 1931.

Goldschmidt, Adolph. "Pseudo-Gothic Spanish Ivory Triptychs…," The Journal of the Walters Art Gallery, p. 49. 1943.

Gräff, W. "Die Sprungbildung Als…," Pantheon, VII, pp. 32-36. January, 1931.

Grancsay, S.V. "Exhibition of Forgeries," Metropolitan Museum of Art Bulletin, XXVII, p. 46. February, 1932.

Grice, J.W.H. "Faking and Selling Chinese Antiques," Country Life, CXVI, pp. 350-351. July, 1954.

Grundy, Reginald. "Spurious Art," Connoisseur, LVI, pp. 135-138. March, 1920.

Gugliemi, S. "Reporting on the Spurious Nature of a Shang Dynasty Bronze," Princeton Museum Record, XXVII, 1, pp. 3-12. 1968.

Hachman, Rolfe. "…Zwei Falschungen Aus Einer Munchner Goldschmidewerkstatt," Germania, XXXVI, pp. 436-446. 1958.

Hansen, Fritz. "Gefälschte Kunstwerke," Das Wissen. 1921.

Harrison, J. "…A Study of Famous Forgeries," Artist, XLI, pp. 84-86. June, 1951.

Hayward, J.F. "Konrad Fecit…," Connoisseur, CXXII, pp. 8-13. September-December, 1948.

Held, J.S. "Stylistic Detection of Fraud," Magazine of Art, XLI, pp. 179-182. May, 1948.

Hepper, F.N. "A Late 18th Century Forgers…," British Numismatist, XXVIII, pp. 422-423. 1957.

Hill, G.F. "The Nobleman and the Forger," Burlington Magazine, XII, pp. 42-47. October, 1907.

Holmes, William H. "On Some Spurious Mexican Antiquities…," Smithsonian Institution Annual Report. 1889.

Hoving, Thomas. "The Game of Duplicity," Metropolitan Museum of Art Bulletin, XXVI, pp. 241-246. 1967-1968.

Isnard, Guy. "La Jaconde et les 'Jaconde'," Jardin des Arts, p. 375. April, 1957.

Ivins, W.M. "Some Notes on Fakes," Magazine of Art, XLI, p. 168. May, 1948.

Janson, H.W. "Hildburgh Relief: Original or Copy?" Art Bulletin, XXX, p. 143. June, 1948.

Jayne, H.H.F. "Chinese Forgery too T'ang to be T'ang," International Studio, XCIV, p. 43. January, 1930.

Keck, S. "Laboratory Detection of Fraud," Magazine of Art, XLI, pp. 172-178. May, 1948.

Knowles, J.A. "Forgeries in Stained Glass," Connoisseur LXXVI, p. 207. August, 1928.

Knowles, J.A. "The Detection of Forgeries of Old Glass," Connoisseur, LXIX, pp. 201-208. August, 1924.

Kurz, Otto. "The Bonus Events…," Journal of the Warburg Institute, XXV, pp. 335-337. 1962.

Kurtz, Otto. "…Art Forgeries from the Renaissance to the Eighteenth…," The Royal Society of Arts Journal, CXXI pp. 518-519. January, 1973.

Lane, A.S. "The Case of the Careless Collector," Art in America, LIII, pp. 90-95. October, 1965.

Lapouge, Gilles. "Gefälschte Bilder, Stein, Hanschriften, Antares, 8, pp. 60-62. 1956.

Laurie, A.P. "A New Way of Detecting Art Forgeries," Scientific American. 1918.

Laurie, A.P. "Crackles and Forgeries of. Primitives, Connoisseur, LXXXI, pp. 157-161. July, 1928.

Laurie, A.P. "Rembrandt Authenticity…," Creative Art VIII, pp. 43-45. January, 1931.

Laurie, A.P. "Various Phases of Art Forgery," Art News XXIX, p. 17. March, 1931.

Lawrence, W.J. "The Prince of Wale's Gift to Ireland," Connoisseur, XII, 191, pp. 176-178. July, 1905.

Lee, R.W. "Concerning Reproduction Glass," American Collector, VII. June 1938.

Leeuwenberg, Jaap. "Early Nineteenth Century Gothic Ivories," Aachner Kunstblätter, XXIX. 1969.

Lemaire, J. "A Propos des Faux d'Amsterdam…," Gazette des Beaux-Arts, III, 4. December, 1930.

Leporini, H. "Gefälschte Kunstwerke," Pantheon, XX, pp 352-354. November, 1937.

Lessing, Alfred. "What is Wrong with a Forgery?" Journa of Aesthetics, XXIII, pp. 461-471. 1964.

Levantal, P.R. "L'Affaire Vermeer Rebondit," Connaissance Arts, 237, pp. 90-101. November, 1971.

Levy, M. "Attributions and Valuations," Studio, CLXII, pp 20-23. January, 1962.

Lindstrom, Arne. "Om Förfalskingar I Finland," Ateneumin II, 2, pp. 25-26. 1957.

Low-Beer, S. "Some Doubtful Lacquers," Oriental Art, IV pp. 271-274. Winter, 1967.

Lught, Fritz. "Echt Oder Unecht?" Festscher E. Trautscholdt pp. 11-14. 1965.

Mackey, M.M. "Fake Antique in Peiping," Asia, XXXVIII 70. January, 1938.

Mackenna, F. "Reproductions and Fakes of Chelsea…," Apollo, LV, pp. 21-22. 1952.

Madersbacher, F. "Antiquidades Modernas," Habitat, LXIV pp. 34-38. 1961.

Magazine of Art, XLI, 5. May, 1948. (special issue on forgeries)

Mann, Klaus. "Les Dessous De L'Affaire Van Meegeren," Age Nouveau, 29, pp. 64-71. 1948.

Marka, Alfred. "The Picture at Chatsworth...," Burlington Magazine, X, pp. 383-384. March, 1907.

Maskell, A. "Forgeries and Imitations of Works of Art," Art Journal, LVIII, pp. 289-295. 1906.

Massen, C.G. Von. "Falscherkunst Aus Eitelkeit," Kunstsammler, I, 1, p. 59. 1930.

Mathey, Francois. "Vrai Ou Faux," Medecine de France, 62, pp. 17-32. 1955.

Meder, Joseph. "Dürer-Kopisten Und Dürer-Kopien," Der Kunstwanderer. 1922.

Mesuret, R. "Les Faux Goya...," Revue du Louvre, IV, pp. 183-194. 1963.

Michel, A. "Le Pseudo Benivieni," Les Arts, pp. 14-17. May, 1903.

Mire, G. De. "Faux Tableaux," L'Art Vivant, 168, pp. 34-35. January, 1933.

Morey, C.R. "The Silver Casket of San Nazaro in Milan," American Journal of Archaeology, XXIII, pp. 101-125. 1919.

Musper, A. Th. "Falschungen Und Verfälschungen In De Bildenden Kunst," Kunstchronik, VII, p. 271. 1954.

Myers, G.H. "Fakes, Forgeries and Falsification," Magazine of Art, XL, p. 80. February, 1947.

Neuburger, Alfred. "Kunstwissenschaftliche Kriminalistik," Welt Und Wissen. January, 1922.

Neugass, Fritz. "Enthullüngen Von Kunstfälschungen in Amerika," Weltkunst, XXXVII, 537. 1967.

Neugass, Fritz. "...Elmyr de Hory," Kunstwerk, XXII, 5-6, pp. 13-15. February, 1969.

Noel, Barnard. "The Incidence of Forgery Amongst Archaic Chinese Bronzes," Monumenta Serica, XXVII, p. 91. 1968.

North, S.K. "Old Masters and X-Rays," Burlington Magazine, LVI, p. 194. April, 1930.

Oman, Charles. "False Plate of Medieval England," Apollo, LX, pp. 74-75. 1952.

Panofsky, Erwin. "Kopie Oder Fälschung?" Zeitschrift fur Bildende Kunst, LXI, pp. 221-244. September, 1927.

Panofsky, Erwin. "Kopie Oder Fälschung?" Zeitschrift fur Bildende Kunst, LXII, pp. 54-67. June, 1928.

Parlasca, Klaus. "Mosaikfälsichung," Mitteilungen des Deutscher Archeologichen Institue — Römische Abteilung, LXVI, p. 155. 1954.

Parsons, H.W. "Art of Fake Etruscan Art," Art News, LX, 10, pp. 34-37. February, 1962.

Philip, H. "...Greek Head Bought in Constantinople," Antiques, XL, p. 214. October, 1944.

Plenderleith, H.J. "Fakes and Forgeries in Museums," Museum Journal, LII, pp. 143-148. September, 1952.

Pomp, A.E. "Fälschlich Michelangelo Zugeschriebene Zeichnungen," Zeitschrift fur Bildende Kunst. 1927-1928.

Porada, E. "Forged North Syrian Seals," Archaeology, X, p. 143. June, 1957.

Raborg, Martin. "Falskt Eller Äkta...?" Konstrevy, XXVIII, 6, p. 275. 1952.

Raynor, V. "Rodin Drawings at the Guggenheim," Art in America, XL, p. 35. May, 1972.

Reff, Theodore. "Copyist in the Louvre 1850-1870," Art Bulletin, XLVI, 4, pp. 552-563. December, 1964.

Reff, Theodore. "New Light on Degas' Copies," Burlington Magazine, pp. 250-258. June, 1964.

Reineking, Gisela Von Bock. "Steinzeug-Nachahvrung, Nachbildung Oder Fälschung," Keramos, XLIX, p. 3. July, 1970.

Remach, Salomon. "Two Forged Miniatures of Joan of Arc...," Burlington Magazine, XIV, pp. 356-357. March, 1909.

Renkins, J.A. "Picture Forgeries," Scotish Art Review, II, pp. 27-28. 1948.

Rewald, J. "False Maillol Drawings on Market," Art News, XLV, p. 6. April, 1946.

Rewald, J. "Modern Fakes of Modern Pictures...," Art News, LII, 1, pp. 16-21. March, 1953.

Richter, G.M. "Forgeries of Greek Sculpture," Metropolitan Museum of Art Bulletin, XXIV, pp. 3-5. January, 1929.

Richter, G.M. "Limitations of the Gentle Art of Faking," Art News, XXXII, p. 14. November, 1933.

Ring, G. "Fälschungspsychose," Zeitschrift fur Bildende Kunst, LXIV, pp. 86-88. March, 1931.

Rodde, C. "Le Probleme Du Plagiat...," Arts, V. August, 1946.

Roe, Fred. "Genuine or Forgery...," Connoisseur, V, 86, pp. 76-85. 1930.

Roe, F. G. "Pickwick in America," Connoisseur, CVII, pp. 111-114. March, 1941.

Rorimer, J. J. "Forgeries of Medieval Stone Sculpture," Gazette des Beaux-Arts, XXVI, pp. 195-210. July/December, 1944.

Ross, E. B. "Antiques Made to Order," Philadelphia Magazine, LXII, 2, p. 68. November, 1971.

Rousseau, Theodore. "The Stylistic Detection of Forgeries," Metropolitan Museum of Art Bulletin, XXVI, pp. 247-252. 1967-1968.

Rowe, L. E. "Forgeries and the Collector," American Magazine of Art, XVIII, pp. 183-186. April, 1927.

Rowe, J. H. "Forged Tiahuanaco-Style Keros," American Antiquity, XX, pp. 392-393. April, 1955.

Rucker-Embden, Oskar. "Note on the Counterfeiting of T'ang and Sung Porcelain," Ostasiatische Zeitschrift, XIV, 4, pp. 151-156. July, 1927.

Russel, John. "La Farce De Van Meegeren," L'Oeil, 14, pp. 5-11. 1956.

Sacchi, F. "Antiche Frodi Monetarie," Emporium, LXXXII, pp. 213-219. October, 1935.

Sack, H. "Authenticity in American Furniture," Art in America, XLVIII, 2, pp. 72-75. Summer, 1960.

Savage, G. "Collector Versus Forger…," Studio, CLXI, p. 195. May, 1961.

Savage, G. "Are Forgeries so Frequent?" Studio, CLXIV, pp. 150-152. October, 1962.

Savage, G. "Uncovering the Forgers Method," Studio, CLXXIV, pp. 178-179. October, 1967.

Schedlman, Hans. "Konrad Fecit…," Connoisseur, CXXII, pp. 8-13. 1948.

Schmidt, Robert. "Verfäschte Möbel," Der Kunstwanderer. 1919.

Schurr, G. "More Picture Fakes," Connoisseur, CLXV, 189. July, 1967.

Seidlitz, W. de. "Artistic Property and Forgeries," Gazette des Beaux-Arts, XIV, 3, pp. 317-334. 1895.

Seidel, L. "A Romantic Forgery," Art Bulletin, L, pp. 33-42. March, 1968.

Selligrad, Rolf. "Original, Reproduktion, Kopia Multi, Simili," Kunstüannen, II, pp. 12-13. 1967.

Shapiro, Maurice L. "Renaissance or Neoclassic…,?" Art Bulletin, XLIV, pp. 131-135. 1962.

Soper, A. C. "…The Ku That Was Too Good To Be True," Atribus Asiae, II, pp. 200-210. 1970.

Soria, M. S. "Unrecorded French Primitive…," Connoisseur, CXVII, pp. 126-127. June, 1946.

Sotheby & Co. "Meissen Porcelain Wares," Art Market, X, 5. July, 1970.

Steege, K. R. "Jenni Acquitted of Smuggling 'The Madonna'…," Art News, XXVIII, pp. 23-24. December, 1929.

Stendall, J. A. S. "Flint Jack-Forger of Antiquities," Museum Journal, XL, pp. 53-55. July, 1944.

Swarzensky, G. "Art and Forgery," Magazine of Art, XLI, pp. 162-167. May, 1948.

Symonds, R. W. "Forged Furniture," Old Furniture, II, pp. 152-162. December, 1927.

Teal, Gardner. "Fraudulent Antiques," American Homes and Gardens, XII, pp. 132-136. April, 1915.

Tietze, Hans. "Die Frage Der Expertisen," Kunst und Kunstler. 1927.

Tietze, Hans. "The Psychology and Aesthetics of Forgery in Art," Metropolitan Museum Studies, V, pp. 1-19. 1936.

Todd, Marion. "Solving the Problem of Art by X-Ray," American Magazine of Art, XVII, pp. 578-580. November 1926.

Toesca, Elena B. "Il Cosiddetto Omero Degli Uffizi," Bolletino D'Arte, XXXVIII, pp. 307-309. October, 1953.

Ulitzsch, Ernst. "Autographenfälschungen," Der Sammler. 1921.

Valentiner, W. R. "An Early Forger," Art in America, I, pp. 195-208. 1913.

Valentiner, W. R. "Statement Concerning Bust Supposed Work of Mino Da Fiesole," Art News, 29, p. 13. May, 1931.

Van Holst, Niels. "Kunstfalschungen in Alter Und Neuer Zeit," Weltkunst, XXIII, 3, p. 4. 1952.

Veth, Cornelis. "Ean Beproeving En Een Proefstuk," Maanblad Voor Beeldende Kunsten, XXII, pp. 22-23. 1946.

Voss, H. "Science Fails in Rembrandt Test," Art News, XXIX, p. 3. April, 1931.

Wallis, Whitworth. "David Cox Forgeries," Connoisseur, XII, 186, pp. 55-56. July, 1905.

Watson, J. "Genuine and Counterfeit," Magazine of Art, XXXIII, pp. 37-46. June, 1940.

Whiting, F. A. "Dossena Forgeries," Cleveland Museum Bulletin, 16, pp. 66-67. April, 1929.

Whiting, F. A. "Tradition, Influence, Imitation," Magazine of Art, XXXII, pp. 94-95. February, 1939.

Wild, A. M. de. "Scientific Examination of Pictures," Formes, VII, pp. 15-16. July, 1930.

Wilpert, Joseph. "Early Christian Sculpture…," College Art Bulletin, IX, pp. 84-141. December, 1926.

Wiske, Eva. "Das Falsche in Der Kunst," Maltechnik, LXI, pp. 109-115. 1955.

Woodward, A. "Mexican Pottery Faking," Los Angeles Museum Quarterly, II, p. 13-18. 1948.

Wolf, B. "…Van Meegeren's Forgeries," Art Digest, XX, 18. January, 1946.

Zouboff, V. "Les Faux Van Gogh," Gazette des Beaux-Arts, X, 2. June, 1932.

Zurcher, E. "Imitation and Forgery in Ancient Chinese Printing and Calligraphy," Oriental Art, I, pp. 141-146. Winter, 1955.

SOME PREVIOUS EXHIBITIONS OF FAKES AND FORGERIES

Fakes and Reproductions, Pennsylvania Museum, Harrisburg, 1916.

Austellung gefälschte Kunstwerk, Kunsthistorische Museum, Vienna, September-October, 1923.

Counterfeits, Imitations and Copies of Works of Art, Burlington Fine Arts Club, London, 1924.

Sculpture by Alceo Dossena, National Art Galleries, Inc., New York, March 9, 1933.

Copies des Maitre, Kunst Museum Basel, September-November, 1937.

Art Genuine or Counterfeit? Fogg Art Museum, Cambridge, Massachusetts, 1940.

Vals or Echt? Stedlijk Museum, Amsterdam, 1953.

True or False? Corning Museum of Glass, Corning, New York, 1953-55.

Le "Musee" de Faux Artistique, Salon Artistique de la Police, Paris, August, 1954.

Forgeries and Deceptive Copies, The British Museum, London, 1961.

Art: Authentic and Fake, Graham Gallery, New York, May, 1967.

Fakes and Frauds, Madison Art Center, Madison, Wisconsin, November-December, 1967.

Fakes, Frauds and Forgeries, Portland Art Museum, Portland, Oregon, February, 1969.

Know What You See, The Renaissance Society of the University of Chicago, Chicago, October-November, 1970.

Buyer Beware, Martin Gordon Gallery, New York, Fall, 1972.

Mistaken Identity, Heckscher Museum, Huntington, L.I., New York, December-January, 1973.

Problems of Authenticity in Nineteenth and Twentieth Century Art, The Art Museum, Princeton University, June 1-30, 1973.

PHOTO CREDITS

Cat. 27   **Relief of Amenhotep I,** Courtesy of Museum of Fine Arts, Boston.

Cat. 142   Honoré Daumier, **The First Bath,** Courtesy of The Detroit Institute of Arts, Detroit.

Cat. 222   Paul Cezanne, **Mont Sainte-Victoire,** Courtesy of The Phillips Collection, Washington, D.C.

Cat. 233   Modern Italian Paperweight, Munroe Studios, Inc., Neenah, Wisconsin.

5000 copies were printed by Kolorpress, Inc.
on Vintage Velvet Offset.
The type was set in Koronna Alphatype.

Ruth Dean, Designer